Taxes

The Best Tax Shelter of Them All...

If you own your business, you can take advantage of certain tax strategies to substantially improve your cash flow *and* the quality of your life.

For example, you can have your corporation start a medical reimbursement plan for employees. *Rationale:* The only medical expenses you can deduct on your *personal* tax return are those that exceed 7.5% of adjusted gross income (AGI). So if your AGI is $40,000 and you have medical expenses of $1,000, you're $1,000 out-of-pocket—with no tax benefit whatsoever. But if your company reimburses you, it *can* deduct the $1,000. *Net cash outlay:* $660 if the company is in the 34% tax bracket.

This strategy works only if the plan applies equally to all employees. If it is limited to top officers, they will be taxed as though the reimbursements were salary income. *Caution:* In the case of shareholders, dividend treatment may result (see below). But even that isn't necessarily terrible. You're still better off paying $660 in taxes than $1,000 in medical bills.

The way you take money out of your company makes a difference in your taxes. Dividends are taxed twice—once to your company (because they aren't deductible) and once to you. Salaries are taxed only once. Obviously, the more of your total compensation you take in salary, the better.

There's a limit, though—your salary must be "reasonable." *Guidelines:* Your education, knowledge, expertise. . .and what top executives in similar companies make. If it appears to the IRS that the reason for the compensation is your ownership interest, it's probably a dividend. If, on the other hand, the reason appears to be the blood, sweat and tears you put into the company, it's probably salary.

S corporations are a way around the whole salary vs. dividends problem. An S corporation pays no taxes itself. Instead, the owners pay taxes on their proportionate share of the company's income. For tax purposes, this is really equivalent to receiving all salary and no dividends. *Drawback:* You have to pay the tax on your share of income *whether or not* you take any money out of the company. If your company has loan covenants that *restrict* payment to owners (as many small businesses do), you could have trouble coming up with the cash for taxes.

Perks are another way to use your business to improve your standard of living, and they are nontaxable if you can show they are necessary to your business. That can be tricky. For company cars, you must charge employees fair rental value for any personal use of the car. But the amount you charge can be less than what Hertz charges.

Of course, if a perk fails the necessity test, you can still take a deduction (to the extent your unreimbursed business expenses together with other miscellaneous itemized deductions exceed 2% of AGI) for whatever part of the expense is attributable to business. *Example:* Membership dues for a club at which you do a lot of business entertaining. Be sure you have good documentation for any such claims.

Home offices have been attracting attention from the IRS lately. If the home office is for your convenience rather than the company's, and if you have a place to work elsewhere, you won't be allowed a deduction. *Exception:* If you have a sideline business that produces additional income—like consulting—and use your home office as either a principal place of business or as a place to meet with clients, your deductions for home office expenses will be allowed.

Other areas in which tax laws play favorites with entrepreneurs:

• *Charitable donations.* Give stock you hold in your company to charity, then have your company buy it back. You get a deduction for the full market value of the stock—with no personal cash outlay—and the charity gets cash.

• *Retirement plans.* As a self-employed individual, you can open a Keogh Plan.

Source: Jack Salomon, partner in charge of state tax services at Peat Marwick Main & Co., Park Ave. Plaza, 55 E. 52 St., New York 10055.

Printed in the United States of America

What to Do with Tax Shelter That Starts Showing Profits

Most tax-shelter investors want tax deductions *now.* Few of them look any further ahead. Perhaps they think the deductions and tax losses, which can only be used to offset other passive income, will go on indefinitely. They won't. Even the best tax-shelter deal can become a tax liability.

Here's why:

Tax shelters "mismatch" income and deductions. In the early years, deductions predominate. You get a tax loss, or, at least, the *taxable income* is much less than *actual* income. Eventually, however, deductions are used up, and taxable income predominates. There may even be a *phantom gain*—tax income but no actual income. Somewhere along the line is the *crossover point.* Here the problem becomes: *How do you bail out in the most advantageous way?*

Selling

If the shelter (or your interest in it) is sold, you will realize a *taxable gain.* The gain equals the proceeds of the sale, minus the property's tax basis, which by then is probably greatly reduced. Proceeds include not only the money you get, but also any liabilities taken over by the purchaser—*discharge of indebtedness.*

Unfortunately, the gain will no longer be taxed at favorable capital-gain rates. It will be taxed as ordinary income with a special 28% ceiling on the tax rate.

Giving

You may want to give away your interest. If the gift is large enough, it may be subject to gift tax. And if the property is subject to liabilities, there may be income tax consequences.

Example: The tax basis of your shelter interest is $10,000. Your share of shelter liabilities is $15,000. Your gift will result in taxable income of $5,000 ($15,000 for discharge of indebtedness less $10,000 basis).

If you give your interest to charity, you can get a charitable deduction of the value of the gift minus the liabilities. But you will have a taxable gain, just as you would for a noncharitable gift (more, actually, as gain on charitable gifts is calculated differently). And charities may be unwilling to accept the gift. *Reason:* Under some sections of the tax law, income from the shelter might be considered taxable, even in the hands of a charitable organization.

Incorporating

You can form a corporation and transfer your shelter interest to it, thereby deflecting the income to a separate taxable entity—the corporation. If, however, the shelter interest is subject to liabilities greater than basis, the difference will be taxable when the transfer to the corporation is made. That is, unless you are willing to transfer enough cash or other property to make the new corporation's tax-basis at least as high as the liabilities, it will take over.

Example: Your shelter interest has a tax-basis of $10,000 and is subject to $25,000 in liabilities. You also own some property with a basis of $15,000 and no liabilities. If you transfer both properties to the new corporation, there's no tax. (*Total liabilities:* $25,000. *Total basis:* $25,000.)

Whether it's smart to put different types of property into the same corporation is something you have to decide. (You can't ignore the possibility of future corporate bankruptcy due to the shelter's tax liabilities.) Also, corporate tax rates may be higher than your individual tax rate.

Making the Most of Your Medical Deductions

Although medical expenses are deductible only to the extent that, in total, they exceed 7.5% of adjusted gross income, the IRS and court decisions have expanded the definition of medical costs that can be deducted from personal income taxes. Plan ahead to take advantage of as many medical expenses as possible.

Medical deductions can be taken for the costs of diagnosis, the treatment or prevention of a disease, or for affecting any structure or function of the body. Limitation: Treatment must be specific and not just for general health improvement.

Example: The IRS successfully denied taxpayers deductions for the cost of weight-control and stop-smoking classes that were designed to improve general health, not to treat a specific ailment or disease. On the other hand, a person with a health problem specifically related to being overweight, such as high blood pressure, might be allowed the deduction.

If an employer tells an overweight employee to lose weight or leave, and the boss has previously enforced such a rule, the plump employee can deduct the cost of a weight-loss program, because money spent to help keep a taxpayer's job is deductible. The IRS says it will allow a deduction if two physicians prescribe a weight-reduction program for the treatment of hypertension, obesity, or hearing problems. The same could go for a person whose doctor certifies that a stop to cigarette smoking is necessary for a specific medical reason (such as emphysema).

The same logic applies to home improvements.

The cost of a swimming pool would be deductible if it is specifically necessary for a person who has polio, as would the cost of an elevator for a heart patient.

Caution: Only the actual cost (over the increase in value to the property) is deductible. The IRS makes taxpayers subtract from the cost of an improvement the amount that the feature adds to the value of the residence.

Example: If a swimming pool costs $10,000, but adds $4,000 to the value of the property, only $6,000 would be tax-deductible. To determine the value, have the property appraised before and after the improvement. (The appraisal fee is tax-deductible as a miscellaneous itemized deduction to the extent allowed by the Tax Reform Act of 1986.)

Medical or business? Because medical costs are deductible only after they exceed 7.5% of a taxpayer's adjusted gross income, it is tempting to declare them as business expenses. Trap: The IRS rarely allows those business deductions. But there is a sizable gray area. A professional singer was once not allowed to deduct the cost of throat treatments as a business expense, but an IRS agent did allow a deduction for a dancer who found it necessary to her career to have silicone breast implants.

Medically unproven treatment is generally deductible, since the IRS has taken the position that it cannot make judgments in the medical field. Example: Laetrile treatments are deductible if the taxpayer receives them legally. Disallowed: A deduction for the cost of a food processor for a special diet consisting of vegetables. Or a special vitamin-enriched diet, even though the taxpayer is diabetic.

Deductions for medical expenses of married children are sometimes possible, provided you contributed more than half of the child's support. How it works: The daughter of a highly paid executive ran up medical bills of more than $5,000. She married later that year and filed a joint return with her husband. Nevertheless, her father was allowed to deduct the cost of treatment on his return for the year, even though the daughter didn't qualify as a dependent.

Education: The IRS draws a hard line on deductibility of special schooling for children with medical problems. Not deductible: The cost of attending a school with smaller classes, even for a child with hearing or sight problems. To be eligible to make such a claim, the school would have to offer special programs for children with specific disabilities. Approved by the IRS: A deduction for the full cost of sending a child to a boarding school equipped to handle deaf children with emotional problems. Denied by the IRS: A deduction for extra costs, including travel, that was claimed by a parent who sent his deaf child to a distant public school that was better equipped than the local public school to handle such students.

Other deductible costs: Birth-control pills and other prescription drugs, vasectomies, legal abortions.

No longer deductible: Unnecessary cosmetic surgery.

Source: Sidney Kess, partner, director of tax planning and policy, Peat Marwick Main & Co., CPAs, 55 East 52 Street, New York 10055.

Unusual Medical Deductions

Payments have been held to be deductible when made to:

- An untrained companion hired to look after an invalid's needs.
- An acupuncturist, even though the state medical association did not recognize acupuncture as a form of medicine.
- A Christian Science practitioner, even though the payer wasn't seeking medical help.
- Social Security, taxes on the wages paid to a private nurse.

In addition, deductions have been allowed for the cost of:

- Whiskey prescribed by a physician to relieve pain.
- A wig prescribed by a psychiatrist for a patient upset by hair loss.
- Extra costs for salt-free or other special food prescribed by a doctor.
- A stereo for a person confined to the house by multiple sclerosis.
- Hand controls for the care of a handicapped person.
- A guide dog for a blind person.
- A car telephone for a person who may require instantaneous medical help.
- Transportation to and from an Alcoholics Anonymous center.
- Lip-reading instructions for a person hard of hearing.
- The extra cost of braille editions of books for a blind person.
- A reader to assist a blind businessperson at the job.
- Insurance on contact lenses for a person who requires them.
- Extra electricity costs for medically necessary equipment, such as a whirlpool or central air conditioning.
- Travel expenses made necessary by illness. *Example:* The fare to the Mayo Clinic. Also deductible:

Travel expenses for a nurse to accompany the patient or even for a spouse who performs medical services. Doubtful: The cost of living in or moving to a more healthful climate.

• The portion of a housekeeper's salary that goes toward the medical care of a sick resident.

Paying Your Child a Tax-Deductible Allowance

Paying your children to work in your business is a good way of providing tax-deductible allowances. A child with no other income can earn up to $3,250 tax free (indexed for inflation).

Caution: Keep very good records of the type of work they do and the hours they put in. The mere fact that you pay wages to your children won't trigger an audit. Their pay is lumped in with wages of other employees on your return. But if you are audited for some other reason, the IRS is likely to question this expense. Be prepared to show the pay was reasonable.

Personal Deduction for Corporate Donation

There is a way for owners of closely held companies to use *company funds* to get a charitable deduction on their *personal* income tax returns. The owner gives the charity stock in his company. Subsequently the company redeems the stock from the charity. *Advantage:* A 100% owner would not give up any ownership interest in the company, since his interest in the company after the charity is redeemed would still be 100%. *How a bailout works:* The owner makes an *informal* agreement with the charity to offer the stock for redemption shortly after the charity receives it. The owner gives the stock to the charity. He takes a deduction on his personal return for the fair market value of the stock. A week or so later, the company redeems the stock from the charity. If the transaction is properly handled, the stock's redemption will not be taxed as a dividend to the owner. *Caution:* The agreement with the charity must be *informal.* The charity must not be under a binding obligation to let the company redeem the stock. It must have the legal right to retain the stock or to sell it to an outsider. *Tax rule:* Normally, if a 100% shareholder in a closely held company has some of his stock redeemed, income from the redemption will be taxed to him as a dividend. But the IRS has agreed that a redemption will not be considered a dividend if it is handled by an *informal* prearranged plan with a charity. Such a transaction *must* be structured properly to ensure the desired tax results. Check with your accountant or attorney.

Source: Tom C. Kline, CPA, 330 W. 58 St., New York.

Wedding Gift from IRS

A parent who provides over half of a child's support can claim a dependency exemption if the child is under 19 or a full-time student ($2,000 indexed for inflation for the tax years after 1988). The cost of a child's wedding is considered support. So even if the child lives with a spouse after marriage, the wedding may push the parent's support cost over the 50% mark and entitle the parent to the exemption. *Drawback:* The newlyweds cannot file a joint return for the year, nor can the child claim the personal exemption for himself.

Source: *Revenue Ruling* 76–184.

New Trap for Charity Givers

The holding period for long-term assets has been increased by Tax Reform. Securities and other property bought in 1988 or later must be held for *more than one year* (rather than six months) to qualify as long-term. Taxpayers who make charitable donations of properties that have increased in value can get a deduction for full market value—but only if they owned the property for the long-term period. Otherwise they can deduct no more than the original cost. *Smart giving:* Don't donate appreciated securities (or other property) bought after December 31, 1987, until you've owned them at least a year and a day. *Note:* There have been numerous proposals to amend Tax Reform and restore favorable tax treatment for long-term gains—another reason to be aware of the new rule.

Deductible Gambling Losses

With luck, you might win big. *Trap:* Winnings are taxable, and winnings over $600 are reported to the IRS.

The tax can be cut by netting the gain against gambling losses, but few people document their losings. *Result:* A person who scores a big win may wind up paying tax on the gain without getting any benefit from his losses. He may wind up paying extra tax even if he *lost more than he won* over the entire year.

Better way: Keep tabs on your gains *and* losses. The IRS recommends wagering tickets, cancelled checks, credit records, bank withdrawal statements and credit receipts as proof. An accurate *diary* is also recommended.

Bottom line: The result of *all kinds* of gambling is netted at year-end to determine the size of any gain. So if you are planning to be lucky at all this year, keep records for the *entire* year.

Source: Dr. Robert S. Holzman, professor emeritus of taxation at New York University, and the author of *Estate Planning: The New Golden Opportunities.* Boardroom Books, Millburn, NJ 07041.

Deductible Commuting

Most commuting expenses aren't deductible, but if a person works at least *two jobs in the same day,* the cost of traveling from first job to second job is deductible as a business expense to the extent that when added to all your other business expenses, they exceed 2% of AGI. (Still can't deduct travel from home to first job or from second job back home.)

Parents Supported by More Than One Child: Who Takes Deduction?

When brothers and sisters support a parent, plan things so that one of them can deduct the parent's medical expenses. *Here's how:*

First step: File a multiple support declaration (Form 2120). Where several people contribute, this form designates the one who can take the exemption. If they pay at least 10% each, but nobody gives as much as half, any *one* of them can take the exemption *if* the others agree.

Second step: The one claiming the exemption should pay doctor bills directly and make clear (on the check) that his contribution is *earmarked* for medical expenses. Then he can deduct the parent's medical expenses on his tax return. *Remember:* Medical expenses can be deducted only for yourself, your spouse and your dependents. You can't take a deduction for medical expenses paid for somebody else unless you can *properly* claim the person as a dependent.

Divorce and the IRS

Two basic tax principles to keep in mind:

First, cash alimony payments are tax deductible. If payments in any year exceed $10,000 no part will be deductible unless the divorce or separation agreement provides that the payments be made for at least six years, except if either spouse dies or the payee spouse remarries. No other payments are deductible. *Exception:* Either spouse can claim medical expenses for the children, subject to the 7.5% floor on the deductibility of medical expenses.

Second, *if the husband deducts the alimony, the wife must declare it as income.*

Child support, lump sum payments, wife's legal fees, premiums on life insurance policies owned by the husband—all these are *not deductible* by the spouse paying them. And they need not be reported as income by the spouse who receives the payments.

In the still common case among executives where the husband has a large taxable income and the nonworking wife has little or none, it probably makes sense to make all the payments as *alimony* rather than something else. The result is to shift income from the husband's high bracket to the wife's lower bracket. It's essential to prepare carefully several alternative plans, varying the mix among alimony and other types of payments, and figuring the available income from each other after taxes. *Keep in mind that:*

The dependency exemption for a child of divorced or separated parents will be given to the custodial parent unless he or she agrees in writing to waive the exemption. Thus, the father probably can claim them even if they live with the mother. Of course, only one can claim them. (If the husband's tax return comes up for audit, they may track down the wife's return, even if she lives in another IRS district.)

A parent having a child living with him or her may be able to file as a (tax-favored) *head of household* by claiming that child as a dependent.

Conceivably, *both* parents might have *head-of-household* status. This could happen if the younger children stayed with mother, but an older child—away at college full time—stayed with father when home on vacation.

Child support normally stops when the children become independent. *Alimony* often goes on until the wife remarries.

If it's agreed that the husband will pay for the wife's divorce lawyer, estimate fee and add this amount to the alimony that has been negotiated. Then get a deduction for the amount. But don't forget it's income to the wife in that case.

When Home-Office Deduction Costs You More Than It Saves

A home office can be a valuable source of current income tax deductions. *Trap:* Home-office deductions can have adverse tax consequences when the residence is sold. You may not be able to defer the tax on all of your profits from the home's sale. *IRS ruling:* If you were entitled to home-office deductions for the business use of your home in the year you sold it, you can only defer tax on part of the gain. You must allocate the gain between residential use and business use. And you can only defer tax on the residential-use part of your gain. *Exception:* If you took home-office deductions in the past, but not in the year of sale, you may be able to defer paying tax on the whole gain.

Source: Revenue Ruling 82-26, 1928-6 IRB, p.5.

How to Deduct Your Hobby

For your own bottom line, it can make a huge difference whether you operate a hobby as a *hobby* or a *sideline business.* As a hobbyist, your tax deductions are pretty much limited to the amount of income the activity generates. But if you run the hobby as a business, all your expenses are deductible to the extent that when they are added to your other business expenses the total exceeds 2% of AGI even if they *exceed* business income.

Problem: The distinction between a hobby and a business is very fine. When you deduct losses from a business that the IRS could label as a hobby, you must be able to prove that you intended to make a profit.

Hobby or Business

As far as the IRS is concerned, a *business* is an activity engaged in for *profit.* There's no law, however, that says you must actually *make* a profit. The only rule is that you must *intend* to make a profit.

Presumption of law that aids taxpayers: If you show a profit in three of any five consecutive years (two out of seven for breeding, showing, training or racing horses), it is presumed you are engaged in an activity for profit. Although the IRS can challenge the presumption, normally it will not.

You can elect to delay any IRS determination until the first five years are up by filing a special form. But in making this election, you sign a waiver of the three-year statute of limitations for the tax years involved.

Profit Motive

If you don't meet the presumption, the IRS may challenge your deductions as *hobby losses.* It will be necessary for you to prove your good intentions. Checklist of things you should be prepared to show the IRS if your business losses are challenged:

- *You operate in a businesslike manner.* Keep accurate books and records.
- *You instituted new operating procedures* to correct past business practices that resulted in losses.
- *You act professionally.* Show that you hired or consulted with recognized experts in the field, and that you followed their advice.
- *You made a serious effort.* Show that you hired qualified people to run your day-to-day operation. Remember, no rule says *you* must devote 40 hours a week to your sideline business.
- *There is a profit potential.* Even if your business continually produces losses, you can still prove a profit motive by showing that assets you have acquired are expected to appreciate.
- *You have had past successes.* It may help establish a profit motive if you show that in the past you were successfully involved in your current activity.

Doing Business

The IRS will look for tangible indications that you have really embarked on a business enterprise. *Suggestions:*

- Register your business name by filing a *"doing business as"* statement with your local county clerk.
- Use business cards and stationery.
- Take out a company listing in the Yellow Pages.
- Keep a log of the business contacts you've seen during the year.
- Advertise in local papers.
- Send promotional mailings to prospective customers.
- Set up a business bank account.
- Get a business telephone.
- Buy a postage meter and a copying machine.
- Hire at least some part-time help.

Tougher Questions

Although it's unfair, the IRS will argue that, since you had other sources of income and could afford to lose money, you could not have had a profit motive. *Your defense:* Nobody goes into business expecting to lose money. Even with your tax deductions, you would have been better off had you done nothing and never started the venture in the first place.

Suppose your business occasionally generates small amounts of income. You could prove a profit motive if you can also show an opportunity to earn a substantial *ultimate* profit in a highly speculative business.

If the IRS can show that you derive personal pleasure from your business, it will count this against you. Businesses that involve horse racing, farming, car racing, and antiques are particularly vulnerable to this kind of attack. *Don't let the IRS bulldoze you.* The courts have consistently held that enjoying what you do is not, by itself, proof that you lack a profit motive.

Source: Randy Bruce Blaustein, Esq., a former IRS agent now with Siegel Rich Pachtman & Co., CPAs, 310 Madison Ave., New York 10017. He is author of *How to Do Business With the IRS,* Prentice-Hall, Englewood Cliffs, NJ 07632, and *Tax Shelters: Shrewd Insights,* Boardroom Books, Millburn, NJ 07041.

Deducting Vacation Costs as Business Expense

Combining a tax-deductible business trip with a short vacation, perhaps with a spouse and family, can be quite attractive. It is important to keep expense categories straight since different tests apply for deductibility.

You can deduct the cost of traveling in the US for business purposes. But you must be able to show that the primary purpose of the trip was business. This does not mean that you cannot combine business with pleasure, only that the primary purpose is business. *Best way to satisfy the IRS:* Prove that more than half of your time at the destination was spent on business.

The all-or-nothing test for travel: Your transportation expenses (airfare, cabs, etc.) are either fully deductible or they cannot be deducted at all. On the other hand, business meal and entertainment expenses at your destination are 80% deductible. Expenses qualify as business meals or business entertainment only if business is actually discussed.

Do not count on deducting the full cost of a trip with your spouse. It is not enough for the IRS that a spouse's presence is a big help to you. *Only your expenses at the meeting site are deductible,* but you are not limited to half of the total costs there. You can still deduct the full amount of what it would cost you to attend alone at the single-room hotel rate, for instance. You can deduct the full cost of services where your spouse's presence does not boost the charge, say, for the taxi from the airport. If you drive to the meeting site, you can deduct almost the full transportation cost. If you fly or take the train, only your ticket is deductible.

For business-vacation combinations of seven days or less to spots outside the US, the regular rules on business travel, explained above, apply. But if you are gone more than seven days and you spend more than 25% of your total time vacationing, you lose a deduction for the portion of your transportation costs that is equal to the number of nonbusiness days divided by the total number of days outside the US.

The rules are tighter for conventions outside the North American area. No costs can be deducted for such a business meeting unless the IRS can be convinced that the selection of the meeting site is reasonable. (In practice, it probably is better to be able to prove that it is more reasonable to hold the convention at the foreign site than in the US.)

No deduction is permitted for travel to investment seminars or investment conventions.

Ship travel can be an asset on a combined business-vacation trip. *Reason:* Days spent in transit count as business days in the allocation formula. *Example:* A two-day business meeting in Paris is followed by a two-week European vacation. If you fly (one day each way), only 22% is deductible (two business days plus two days of travel out of a total of 18 days away). But if you sail (five days each way), 46% is deductible (two business days plus 10 days of travel out of a total of 26 days away).

Good records are needed to justify your deductions. *Required:* Keep a diary in which you record expenses and their business purpose. You must also keep receipts for expenses of $25 or more. The diary alone is sufficient proof for smaller amounts.

Source: Edward Mendlowitz, partner, Mendlowitz Weitsen, CPAs, 310 Madison Ave., New York 10017, and author of *Successful Tax Planning,* Boardroom Books, Millburn, NJ 07041.

Big Tax Refund?

If you got a fat tax refund this year, don't feel too happy about it. It means you overpaid your estimated taxes or had too much withheld from your salary. In effect, you made an interest-free loan to the government, when you could have been using the money for yourself—in an interest-paying bank account.

Trap: The IRS can withhold all or part of your refund to offset a tax liability, a debt to a government agency (for instance, a student loan), or unpaid child support.

What to do: File a new Form W-4 or W-4A to reduce the amount withheld from your salary. If you pay estimated tax, reduce your quarterly payments.

Caution: Don't overdo it. You can be hit with underpayment penalties unless withholding taxes plus estimated tax payments amount to at least 90% of your total tax bill.

Use Your In-Laws to Cut Your Tax Bill

If you've suffered a loss on an investment property, you can't deduct it while keeping the property in the family by selling it to a spouse, brother, sister, parent, grandparent, child, or grandchild. It doesn't matter if the sale is perfectly legitimate. The Tax Code prohibits any loss deduction from a sale to one of these relatives.

Loophole: The Tax Code does *not* consider in-laws to be relatives under this rule. So don't sell to your son or daugther—sell instead to your son-in-law or daughter-in-law (or some other in-law). You'll keep the property in the family and get a deduction too.

You're Always Safe Taking the Standard Deduction, Right? Wrong.

Self-employed people are likely to have their returns audited if they take the standard deduction instead of itemizing personal nonbusiness deductions, especially if their business shows a high gross and a low net. The IRS will suspect that personal deductions have been charged to the business.

Negligence or Tax Fraud?

Failure to report income deposited in a bank could be considered careless. That is punishable by a 5% negligence penalty. But when the omitted income represented deposits made in a bank in a different state, one court regarded the omission as a fraudulent, willful attempt to conceal income.

Source: *Candella et al. vs. United States,* USDC, E. Dist. WI.

Minimizing Chances of Tax Audit

To be perfectly candid, there is no way of being sure that your Federal income tax return won't be audited. Even overpaying won't protect you from IRS scrutiny. Some returns are pulled out by random selection. Others are chosen by Internal Revenue Service computers, which analyze returns to score the likelihood of collecting further. Computers select a return for audit if medical expenses, contributions, property taxes, etc., represent an unusually high percentage of the taxpayer's income (according to nationwide experience). Returns also invite scrutiny when figures do not agree with other information received by the IRS. (A corporation reports on Form 1099 that it paid $2,000 in dividends to a taxpayer, but that taxpayer reports only $1,000.) And returns may be audited by reason of tips provided by tax informants.

But chance of audit can be reduced greatly by following these suggestions:

1. Answer *all* questions on the tax return form.

2. Complete all schedules that are required. Use the words "None" or "Not applicable" where appropriate.

3. Include full documentation of items which are certain to be questioned, such as large casualty losses or large moving expenses. If the IRS asks for that unsupplied substantiation, expect this request to come up with additional questions in other areas of the return at the same time.

4. Send tax returns and other documents to the right office at the right time so that correspondence and personal contact aren't necessary. Once begun, such correspondence or contact is often difficult to end, for one thing leads to another.

5. Don't deduct a type of item that had been disallowed on a previous tax return. The IRS may remember this and look for a repeat.

6. Don't use a tax preparer of dubious character. If the Service, through its investigators, finds a preparer who is grossly incompetent *or worse,* the names of all his clients will be obtained. All of them, however innocent, will have their tax returns checked by experts in this sort of thing.

7. Be certain that the return has the right signatures and identifying numbers. If it is a corporate return, the title of the signer should be one of the officers *authorized by law* to sign.

Many audits are triggered by:

- *Information returns from banks, investments or employers* that show payments (dividends, interest, salaries or fees) that differ from those reported.
- *Unusually large deductions.* The computer flags deductions that are much larger than the *average* amount taken by most taxpayers in the same income group. *Suggestions:* Provide some details on extra large deductions. Big casualty loss? Describe the hurricane or flood, maybe even enclose newspaper clipping. Give dates and details of long illness or serious accident that produced large medical deductions.
- *Unbelievable numbers.* Such as claiming that you held real estate or IBM stock for 25 years and sold it at a loss. Or large deductions and losses that leave no money to live on. Business expenses that are out of line with the amount of gross income or the nature of the business. Or mortgage interest and property tax deductions that are unusual for where you live.

• *Large round numbers.* Raises questions as to whether you just picked an exaggerated number out of the air without supporting documentation.

• *Office at home.* Getting closer scrutiny because the rules are now much tougher.

Important: If IRS strikes gold in auditing a return, it will often go after other members of the family, or partners, employees, other stockholders in the same S corporation.

IRS Hit List

Doctors and *dentists* are high-priority targets. *Items IRS agents look for:* Dubious promotional expenses. If the same four people take turns having lunch together once a week and take turns picking up the tab, a close examination of diaries and logbooks will show this. Agents also take a close look at limited partnership investments, seeking signs of abusive tax shelters. And they take a dim view of fellowship exclusions claimed by medical residents.

Other target occupations:

• *Salespeople:* Outside and auto salespeople are particular favorites. Agents look for, and often find, poorly documented travel expenses and padded promotional figures.

• *Airline pilots:* High incomes, a propensity to invest in questionable tax shelters, and commuting expenses claimed as business travel, make them inviting prospects.

• *Flight attendants:* Travel expenses are usually a high percentage of their total income and often aren't well documented. Some persist in trying to deduct pantyhose, permanents, cosmetics and similar items that the courts have repeatedly ruled are personal rather than business expenses.

• *Executives:* As a group they are not usually singled out. But if the return includes a Form 2106, showing a sizable sum for unreimbursed employee business expenses, an audit *is* more likely. Of course, anyone whose income is over $50,000 a year is a high-priority target just because of the sums involved.

• *Teachers and college professors:* Agents pounce on returns claiming office at home deductions. They are also wary of educational expense deductions because they may turn out to be vacations in disguise.

• *Clergymen:* Bona fide priests, ministers, and rabbis aren't considered a problem group. But if W-2s show income from nonchurch employers, IRS will be on the alert for mail-order ministry scams.

• *Waitresses, cabdrivers, etc.* Anyone in an occupation where tips are a significant factor is likely to get a closer look from the IRS nowadays.

Many people, aware their profession subjects them to IRS scrutiny, use nebulous terms to describe what they do. Professionals in private practice may list themselves as simply "self-employed." Waitresses become "culinary employees," pilots list themselves as "transportation executives." But there's a fine line here. Truly deceptive descriptions could trigger penalties. And if the return *is* chosen for audit, an unorthodox job title for a mundane profession could convince the agent you have something to hide. Then he'll dig all the deeper.

Source: Ralph J. Pribble, a former IRS field agent, president of Tax Corporation of California, 5420 Geary Blvd., San Francisco 94121.

How to Handle an IRS Auditor

The more time you put between initial contact by the IRS and your first appointment with the auditor, the better off you'll be. *Reason:* Revenue agents are under considerable pressure to close their quota of cases within a set period of time. The longer your case has been in the agent's inventory, the more likely he is to rush through the audit—to your advantage.

How to buy time: Telephone to ask for an extension. Do this the day before your appointment, not the day you get the appointment letter. By then, the agent will be booked up with other cases for six weeks or so.

If you're persistent, and you have legitimate reasons for extensions, you can generally postpone the audit for up to six months. *Caution:* Don't ask for a postponement without a good excuse. Stalling can backfire by antagonizing the agent.

Presenting Your Case

Prepare meticulously for the audit. Gather all your receipts for the deductions the IRS has questioned. List each, in detail, on a sheet of paper. Also, meticulously reconstruct cash expenditures for which you don't have receipts. Explain exactly how and when you made those expenditures.

By presenting your case in factual detail, you establish your credibility. And *credibility is everything* at an audit. It will be easier for the auditor to allow nondocumented items if you can show him that you kept some receipts, that you made an effort to comply with IRS rules and regulations, and that you've reconstructed, as best you could, your cash outlays.

T&E Audits

Travel and entertainment is the most commonly audited deduction. *Your goal:* To limit the items the agent examines by persuading him to do a *test check* of your expenses. Let the auditor choose a three-month period for detailed examination. Or talk him into limiting the audit to items over, say, $100. Make sure you can document all items in the test-check period or in the amount. Keep a T & E expense diary. *Double benefit:* A test check cuts down your work in assembling backup data, and it prevents the agent from rummaging through *all* your travel and entertainment expenses.

Keep Talking

Don't expect to walk out of an audit not owing a dime. Your objective is to strike the best possible deal. *To get an auditor to see things your way:* Keep harping on the items he says must be adjusted. Keep talking. Don't give up until he reduces the adjustment. Even the most hardnosed agent will ultimately concede some proposed adjustments if you're stubborn enough. But you must be prepared to give a little, too—to concede items you're weak on, to bargain. Keep in mind that the agent's goal is to close the case and move on to his next audit.

Special Problems

Business audits. If your business is being audited, have it done at your accountant's office, *not* at your home or your place of business. You don't want the auditor to see your standard of living nor run the risk that an employee will say something to the auditor that could hurt you.

Unreported income. A question generally asked at IRS audits is *Have you reported all your income?* Never answer this or other potentially embarrassing questions with a lie. *Deliberately failing to report all your income is a crime. So is lying to an IRS employee.* To avoid incriminating yourself, deflect the question with *Why do you want to know that?* or *I'll get back to you on that later.* The question may not come up again. Another way to avoid answering this question is to not show up for the audit. Then the deductions you've been asked to prove will be automatically disallowed. But you can *appeal* the agent's disallowance at the appeals level of the IRS. At the appeals level, you're generally not asked whether you've reported all your income.

Special agents. Their job is to develop evidence for *criminal* tax cases. If they show up at your door, don't answer *any* of their questions, even seemingly innocuous ones. Tell them to talk with your lawyer. Then retain a lawyer who is knowledgeable in criminal tax matters. *Best:* A former assistant US attorney.

Source: Randy Bruce Blaustein, Esq., a former IRS agent, now with the New York CPA firm, Siegel Rich Pachtman & Co., 310 Madison Ave., New York 10017. Mr. Blaustein is author of *How to Do Business With the IRS,* Prentice-Hall, Englewood Cliffs, NJ 07632, and *Tax Shelters: Shrewd Insights,* Boardroom Books, Millburn, NJ 07041.

Appealing IRS Audit Conclusions

The best forum to fight in, after the audit or examiner level, is the IRS's own Appellate Division. There, taxpayers who disagree with IRS audit conclusions and who can document their position with sound facts have a good chance of getting at least part of what they're asking for, without going to court.

An appeal to the appellate level of the IRS is handled by highly trained IRS personnel called appeals officers. It is the appeals officers' job to settle cases, to see that they don't go to court, while still getting the most they can for the government.

Unlike auditors, who are bound by the regulations and rulings of the IRS, the appeals officer is entitled to consider the hazards of litigation. That is, the chance that the government might lose in court if it litigates a case. If the officer feels that the government has a weak position on the facts, or there are cases in the taxpayer's jurisdiction against the government, odds are that he will concede or agree to a settlement.

The officer has a great deal of leeway. It is possible for a taxpayer to horse-trade and negotiate on individual items with conferees. Typical is for the officer to concede half the tax bill (or a third of the bill) as being deductible. The taxpayer will have to concede the other half or two-thirds.

Some issues that are not likely to be settled at the audit level, but which taxpayers have a good chance of resolving at appeal, are:

- Cash expenditures that the auditor has disallowed for lack of documentation where those expenditures are common in the taxpayer's business.
- Travel and entertainment deductions that are disallowed because the taxpayer does not have all the support the tax law requires. These disallowances can normally be settled on appeal if the amounts are reasonable.
- Business use of property. A taxpayer uses his car in business 75% of the time, say. But the auditor says he hasn't supported his deduction. If the taxpayer can show that he normally uses his car in business, an appeal should be successful.
- Charitable contributions. Large deductions and those involving hard-to-value gifts, such as stock in a closely held business, become battles of appraisals. These often need to be settled on appeal.
- Constructive dividends. Are items of expense paid by a closely held company to an officer-shareholder deductible, or are they a nondeductible preferential dividend?

But do not go up through the appeal process on a lark, hoping for the best outcome. Prepare a decent case. Get sound professional advice. The appeals officers are technically competent people. They are not likely to let anything slip by them.

Do not expect to get 100% of what you ask for. If several issues are taken to appeal, be prepared to concede some as part of the give-and-take negotiations.

Cases that involve questions of fact rather than law have the best chance of being settled because facts lend themselves to compromise. On legal issues, there's less room for negotiation. For every six cases the taxpayer can come up with in support of a legal position, the appeals officer will have six for the government. There's a standoff, which the officer will have no choice but to resolve on the principal of hazards of litigation.

The best approach in dealing with an appeals officer (or an auditor, for that matter) is to give as much factual background as possible. Point out where the auditor was wrong. Support that position with facts. What prevails is a strong factual presentation, forcefully argued.

Source: David E. Lipson, partner in charge of the tax division of the Chicago office of Arthur Andersen & Co.

Scariest Tax Audit Is the One Right After You Die

It is standard operating procedure for the Internal Revenue Service to examine the Federal income tax returns of a decedent for the three years prior to his death.

Unless clear and well-documented work papers can be shown and explained to the IRS by a knowledgeable person familiar with the facts, there are apt to be disallowances because of lack of substantiation.

Can your returns be explained satisfactorily by someone else when you are not available?

Information as to where records are located should not be in the will. Rather, include it in a separate communication to the executor in advance, or leave it among personal possessions.

Source: *Estate Planning: The New Golden Opportunities* by Robert S. Holzman, Boardroom Books, Millburn, NJ 07041.

Banks & Credit Cards

Tricks Banks Play With Interest Rates

Banks teach their loan officers a number of strategies to get an extra ¼% or even ½% from borrowers. *Recognize some of their tricks:*

• Doing the negotiating at the bank, which is familiar territory to the banker, intimidating to the borrower.

• Not mentioning the rate at all, but simply filling it in on the note.

• "Since you need the money today, let's write it up at X%. Then we can talk later about changing it." The banker hopes you'll never bring it up again. He certainly won't.

• Flat statement: "The rate for this type of loan is X%." (Never true except for small consumer loans. There is always room to negotiate.)

• Postponing the rate discussion as long as possible, hoping borrower will weaken under deadline pressure.

• Ego-building. Bank president stops by during negotiations.

• Talking constantly about how little the interest costs after taxes. And comparing it with finance company rates, secondary mortgage rates or the cost of equity capital.

The banker looks at the company's account as a package, including loans, average balances maintained and fees for service. Borrower options: Trade off higher average balances for a lower interest rate on borrowings or vice versa.

The borrower is at a disadvantage because he probably negotiates a loan only once a year or less, while the banker spends full time at it. So prepare carefully for negotiations.

Good tactics for the borrower:

• Ask interest rate question early—in your office, not his. Don't volunteer suggestions.

• Negotiate everything as a package—rate, repayment schedule, collateral, compensating balances. Banker's strategy will be to try to nail down everything else and then negotiate interest rate when the borrower has no more leverage and no room to maneuver.

• Be prepared with an expression of surprise and shock, even rehearse it before a mirror. React that way when the banker mentions the interest rate, no matter what the figure is.

Source: Lawrence T. Jilk, Jr., executive vice president, National Bank of Boyertown, Pa., in *The Journal of Commercial Bank Lending.*

What Banks Don't Tell You

• Banks like to advertise their *effective annual yield,* whereas money-market funds are legally permitted to advertise only the simple interest rates. The long-standing rule inadvertently conceals the fact that money-market funds *do* compound interest on a daily basis. If a bank and a money-market fund pay the *same rate,* the bank will *appear* to offer more by advertising the *effective rate.*

• Some banks say they let you draw on all checks immediately, provided you put up another bank account as collateral. *Catch:* If a check backed by a six-month certificate bounces, the bank can break into the certificate before maturity. If this happens, you will have to pay an interest penalty. *Protection:* Pick a bank that will allow you time to *cover* a bounced check before it takes any money from your time deposit. Be *sure* your bank has this policy before you decide to use a time deposit as collateral.

• Don't bite if the bank offers you a big saving in return for a lump-sum payoff of the old low-interest mortgage on your home. *The catch:* The discount "bonus" comes from principal—not interest—and is taxable income. You will gain a greater return on your money if you set aside the amount sought by the bank and invest it yourself.

• **Checks dated more than six months ago are usually not cashable, no matter how much money the issuer has in the bank. (*Exception:* US Treasury checks are valid indefinitely.)**

• If the amount written on the check in words is different from the amount written in numbers, the bank will pay the sum shown *in words.*

• Be careful when endorsing checks. To prevent loss of money, when sending checks by mail for deposit, write "For Deposit Only" above your signature on the back. That limits the endorsement. An endorsed check with nothing but a signature is the same as cash and may be used by anybody if it's lost or stolen.

Safeguards for Safe-Deposit Boxes

Valuables stored in bank safe-deposit boxes are not automatically protected against loss through burglary, flood or fire. To be compensated for missing valuables, depositors must initiate lawsuits against the bank. The chances of winning are very, very slim.

Safeguards: Buy insurance for the contents of the boxes even though reimbursement levels are low. And most negotiable items, such as securities, bank notes, gold, coins and cash, are not covered.

Alternative: Store stocks and bonds at the brokerage house where they were purchased. These firms have a legal and financial responsibility to guard securities stored with them.

Another option: Open a custody account with a bank. The bank holds securities and other assets in its vault. It collects and credits all dividends, but does not manage the assets. The bank will replace any asset in the vault that is lost, stolen or harmed. Charges are generally based on the size of the account and the composition of the holdings.

When the Bank Can't Bounce a Check

The bank may have to honor a check if it takes too long to bounce it. Uniform Commercial Code requires that the bank take some action by midnight of the business day after it receives the check. But the bank gets more time if there's an emergency beyond its control, for example, computer breakdown.

Cashing a Letter

Letters or telegrams may serve as checks. Requirements: The letter must be addressed to a bank. And it must state that a specific amount is to be paid on demand either to the bearer of the letter or to the order of a named person. Point: If any one of these requirements is not met, the letter will not be valid as a check. Of course, the bank will make its usual effort to verify that the "check" is valid.

Source: *United Milk Prods. Co. V. Lawndale Nat'l Bank,* 392 F. 2d 876, 5 UCC Rep. 143.

Checks Marked "Payment in Full"

If there's no dispute as to the amount, a check tendered for less than the amount due and marked "payment in full" (or the like) may be cashed without prejudicing the right to recover the balance.

If there's a bona fide dispute as to the amount owing, the creditor must be wary. Alternatives: Reject the check and demand full payment. Or: Accept the check but run the risk that payment will be deemed to have settled the disputed claim for the lesser amount. It's easy enough for a debtor who wants to pay less than the amount for which he's billed to create a dispute on the basis of quantitative or qualitative deficiencies in the goods or services supplied.

Stamp the check with a statement to the effect that "Check is accepted without prejudice and with full reservation of all rights under Section 1-207 of the Uniform Commercial Code." The effectiveness of this technique is untested in the courts, but it may help protect a creditor's rights and provide leverage in a settlement.

How to Deposit an Unsigned Check

Write or type the word "over" on the line where the signature would normally appear. On the back, type *lack of signature guaranteed*. . . and add your company's name, and your name and title. Then sign. This guarantees your bank that you'll take back the check as a charge against your account if it isn't honored. Most banks will then process the check and remit the funds. This saves you the trouble of returning the check to your customer for signature.

Source: *Credit & Financial Management,* 475 Park Ave. S., New York 10016.

What VISA and MasterCard Don't Tell You

One VISA card or MasterCard could be very different from another VISA card or MasterCard. What counts is the bank issuing it.

The MasterCard and VISA organizations do not issue credit cards themselves. They provide a clearing system for charges and payments on the cards and license banks to use the VISA or MasterCard name. It is the issuing bank that determines the interest rates and fees.

A bank's name on a credit card does not necessarily mean that it is the bank actually issuing the card. Issuance of credit cards is a high-risk, low-profit business. Seldom does a small bank issue its own.

Generally, a small bank will act as an agent for an issuing bank. The agent bank puts its name on the card, but it is the issuing bank that actually extends any credit.

Aside from costs, this can be important if the cardholder encounters an error. The correction might have to be agreed upon, not by a friendly local banker, but by an unknown, larger institution, perhaps in a different state.

Choosing which card to take is becoming more difficult, because some of the nation's largest banks have begun active solicitation of customers throughout the US. Individuals must be especially careful about accepting any offer that might come in the mail.

A recently discovered quirk in the federal law allows federally chartered out-of-state banks to ignore state usury laws that limit the amount of interest or fees that the issuing bank may charge on its credit cards. In Arkansas, for example, state usury laws prevent local banks from charging more than 10% interest on credit card balances. But a federally chartered out-of-state bank, in lending to Arkansas residents, may charge whatever its home state allows. Even with individual states, the terms on credit cards can vary widely.

Aside from the actual rates and fees, individuals must carefully check the fine print of their contracts. Most banks, for example, do not charge interest on balances stemming from purchases until the customer is billed for such purchases. If the bill on which the charges first appear is paid in full by the stated due date, there is no interest charge to the holder. But some banks, those in Texas, for example, begin charging interest as soon as they receive the charge slip and make payment to the merchant. Thus, interest begins accumulating even before the cardholder receives the bill. These interest charges continue until the bank receives payment from the customer.

Source: Robert A. Bennett, banking correspondent, *The New York Times*.

Credit Cards: Beating the System

Credit cards have become a way of life for most Americans. However, very few people realize the unnecessary costs they incur by not utilizing their cards to their advantage or by not choosing the least expensive card to begin with.

Determine which card is best for you. Banks offering VISA or MasterCard services have a wide variety of fees and interest charges. Some levy a $35 charge, while others will nick you for only $20. Moreover, interest charges for goods purchased range from 18% to 22%. And some banks charge interest from the date of purchase, while others charge no interest if you pay your monthly bill on time.

Watch out, too, for bank cards that bill on a 24-day cycle, which means customers receive 14 bills per year. If you are used to paying all your bills once a month, one of those 14 could easily get delayed in the shuffle. Then you will be charged interest on the missed bill and get a reputation as a slow payer.

Even if the credit terms and service charges are to your liking, find out if there is any time limit on them. Some banks offer attractive deals as part of a special promotion that expires after nine months or a year. Take advantage of such offers—but be ready to switch over to another bank card if it is less expensive once the promotion expires.

Credit cards also can be used as a bargaining chip to receive a discount from a merchant. Merchants typically pay a fee of 2%–7% of your charge when you use your credit card. With an American Express or Diners Club card, they may have to wait a while to get paid. It may be to the advantage of the merchant to go along with your suggestion of a 5% discount if you pay cash.

Another way to beat the system: Take a cash advance on your credit card and pay directly for goods and services, rather than charging them if bank-interest charges are less for cash advances. If you already are being charged interest for merchandise purchases, take a cash advance and switch the balance due to the lower rate.

If no interest charge has yet been levied, then time the cash advance to a day or two before the bill would be past due and pay off the merchandise portion of the bill. *Reason for the timing maneuver:* Cash advances are charged interest from the day that they are taken. Multiple credit cards come in handy if you want to go to the limit of allowable cash advances on each without having to use your card to purchase merchandise at high rates.

If you have gotten in over your head, it may be best to take out a consumer loan to pay off a number of credit-card bills. Although the consumer loan rate may not be much cheaper than the credit-card cash advance rate, it can be significantly cheaper than the card's basic interest rate on merchandise purchases. In addition, since bank credit-card payments are based on a 24-month term, one big advantage to consolidating such debt with a 36-month consumer loan is lower monthly payments.

Source: Edward Mendlowitz, a partner with Mendlowitz Weitsen, CPAs, New York.

Health

Exercises That Can Hurt You

One should be careful in selecting an exercise plan. Correct breathing and posture during exercise are essential. Improper exercising can cause or aggravate injuries. Even basic exercises can be dangerous:

- *Toe-touching:* Doing this with the knees in a locked position and with a rapid bouncing action places tremendous pressure on the lumbar vertebrae. This could result in lower-back pain. Allow your knees to bend slightly, and remain in a hanging-over position for three complete slow, deep breaths. Then straighten slowly. Repeat this three times. Do it without bouncing.
- *Leg lifts:* Performing these while lying on your back and raising both legs at the same time can cause the pelvis to rotate and lead to swayback (the problem of lower-back lordosis). Eliminate this exercise.
- *Sit-ups:* Doing these with straight legs can also contribute to an increased curvature of the lower back. For the abdominal muscles to get a real workout, bend your knees, keep your feet flat on the floor, fold your arms over your chest and curl up to only a 30° angle from the floor.
- *Deep knee-bends:* These can cause injury to knee cartilage. Bending the knees so that they are directly over the feet and the thighs are parallel to the floor will not cause injury.

The important thing to remember is that any repeated movement done in an unnatural position can create problems. Two key areas of the body to be concerned with are the knees and the lower back. If an exercise is painful, perhaps you are doing it improperly, or it is too advanced for you. Or: It may be simply a dangerous exercise.

How Long to Wait Between Hard Workouts

The same *heavy* exercise workout *every day* can promote injury. Each hard workout does some minor damage to muscle tissue, which takes about 48 hours to heal. Muscles also *shorten* as they heal. *Stretching* between exercise sessions helps.

Source: Dr. Gabrial Mirkin, professor of sports medicine, University of Maryland, quoted in *Executive Fitness Newsletter,* 33 E. Minor St., Emmaus, PA 18049, 26 issues.

Medicines That Can Hurt You When You Exercise

Drugs and exercise can be a hazardous combination. *Aspirin* can mask the pain that should tell you to stop. *Antihistamines* can cause drowsiness and strain the heart and muscles. *Decongestants* raise overall blood pressure. *Diuretics* can lead to dehydration and cramping. *Tranquilizers,* besides robbing you of your competitive edge, dull your perception of pain. *Best:* Take a new drug at least twice and gauge your reaction *before* adding the stress of vigorous exercise. And never combine different drugs with exercise without consulting your doctor.

Source: Dr. Richard H. Dominguez, co-medical director, Sports Performance and Rehabilitation Institute, Carol Stream, Ill.

Working Off a Big Meal is Easier Than You Think

Exercising soon after eating is an efficient way to burn off excess calories. *Reason:* Since both eating a good meal and exercising *raise* your body's metabolic rate, you use up more calories exercising *after* a meal than before one. (Conversely, cutting back on calories *lowers* your metabolism and makes you work harder to burn off what you do eat.) *Minimum requirement for working off a meal:* A 20-minute walk within 45 minutes of eating.

Source: David Levitsky and Eva Obarzanek, Division of Nutritional Sciences, Cornell University.

Exercises to Do in the Car

(1) *Double chin:* Lift chin slightly and open and close mouth as though chewing. (2) *Flabby neck:* Move head toward right shoulder while looking straight ahead at the road. Return head to center, then toward left shoulder. (3) *Pot belly:* Sit straight with spine against back seat. Pull stomach in and hold breath for count of 5. Relax, then repeat. The exercise also relieves tension and helps fight sleepiness.

Overdosing on Vitamins

The old advice is still the best—there is no reason to take more than the recommended dietary allowance (RDA) of any vitamin, except for relatively rare individuals who cannot absorb or utilize vitamins adequately.

A megadose is 10 or more times the RDA. This is the level at which toxic effects begin to show up in adults. Even in cases of actual vitamin insufficiency, megadoses are not generally prescribed. Therapeutic doses are generally smaller than 10 times the RDA.

Vitamins are becoming more popular because of a combination of successful merchandising by manufacturers in so-called health magazines, faddism, misinformation, and questionable practices by some professionals.

Most persuasive to hard-nosed executives are enthusiastic testimonials from other executives who have been persuaded by the placebo effect of vitamins that megadoses really do make them feel better.

Some of the medical problems adults may experience as a result of prolonged, excessive intake are:

- Vitamin A. Dry, cracked skin. Severe headaches. Severe loss of appetite. Irritability. Bone and joint pains. Menstrual difficulties. Enlarged liver and spleen.

- Vitamin D. Loss of appetite. Excessive urination. Nausea and weakness. Weight loss. Hypertension. Anemia. Irreversible kidney failure that can lead to death.

- Vitamin E. Research on E's toxic effects is sketchy, but the findings suggest some problems: headaches, nausea, fatigue and giddiness, blurred vision, chapped lips and mouth inflammation, low blood sugar, increased tendency to bleed, reduced sexual function. Ironically, one of the claims of Vitamin E proponents is that it heightens sexual potency.

- The B vitamins. Each B has its own characteristics and problems. Too much B_6 can lead to liver damage. Too much B_1 can destroy B_{12}.

- Vitamin C. Kidney problems and diarrhea. Adverse effects on growing bones. Rebound scurvy (a condition that can occur when a person taking large doses suddenly stops). Symptoms are swollen, bleeding gums, loosening of teeth, roughening of skin, muscle pain.

Vitamin C is the vitamin most often used to excess. Some of the symptoms of toxic effect from Vitamin C megadoses:

- Menstrual bleeding in pregnant women and various problems for their newborn infants.

- Destruction of Vitamin B_{12}, to the point that B_{12} deficiency may become a problem.

- False negative test for blood in stool, which can prevent diagnosis of colon cancer.

- False urine test for sugar, which can spell trouble for diabetics.

- An increase in the uric acid level and the precipitation of gout in individuals predisposed to the ailment.

Better than vitamin pills are:

- Four portions a day of grains (either cereal, bread or pasta).
- Four portions of fruits and vegetables (including at least one fresh fruit or vegetable or fruit juice).
- Two or three portions of milk and milk products.
- Two portions of meat, fish, poultry, eggs, dry beans, peas or nuts.

For people who don't eat properly or want nutrition insurance, take a regular multivitamin capsule containing only the RDA of vitamins.

Source: Dr. Victor Herbert, *Nutrition Cultism: Facts and Fictions*, George F. Stickley Co., Philadelphia.

Vitamin C and Aspirin

These substances should *not* be taken together. Studies at the University of Southern Illinois indicate that combined *heavy doses* produce excessive stomach irritation which could lead to ulcers (especially for those with a history of stomach problems).

Trace Mineral Supplements

Sometimes these supplements can be dangerous. *Reason:* These elements are in delicate balance in your body. It's easy to overdose, and an excess of one can lead to a deficiency of another. *Better:* Eat foods rich in these nutrients. *Examples:* Meat, liver and eggs (zinc and selenium). Oysters, nuts and chocolate (copper). Brown rice, tea and coffee (manganese).

Pros and Cons of Vasectomy

According to the most recent studies, vasectomies have no effect on the production of testosterone or other hormones. The body still produces both sperm (which is reabsorbed by the body) and seminal fluid (which is ejaculated).

Vasectomies are considered so safe and simple that they're generally performed under local anesthetic in a doctor's office or in a clinic. The doctor makes one or two incisions in the scrotum through which each sperm-carrying tube (*vas deferens*) can be lifted out, cut, and closed, thus blocking the passage of sperm. The operation takes 20 minutes. *Cost:* $100–$250 (depending on clinic or physician). Usually covered by Blue Shield or other private medical insurance. If it is performed on Friday afternoon, most men can go back to work on Monday. Best then to wear an athletic supporter and to avoid heavy labor for a week to 10 days. There may be some discomfort for several days. Usually ice packs and aspirin provide all the relief that is needed. Contraception is still necessary for the first 10 to 12 ejaculations after a vasectomy—until two samples of semen, generally taken a week or two apart, show no sperm.

Physical After-Effects

• *Sperm antibodies* develop in about 50% of vasectomized men. One type of antibody immobilizes sperm. The other causes sperm to agglutinate (clump together). These antibodies may prevent restoration of fertility in men whose vasectomies have later been reversed. But it is not yet known for what length of time these sperm antibodies go on being produced and under what conditions the body stops producing them.

• *Increased cholesterol and atherosclerotic placque.* The results of an experiment on monkeys at the Oregon Primate Research Center, which concluded that vasectomies produced increased cholesterol and atherosclerotic placque, were widely publicized. However, there were only five monkeys in the experimental group and the monkeys' diet contained *twice the cholesterol* found in an ordinary human diet. More recent studies belie the connection between vasectomies and atherosclerotic build-up in men.

Reversibility

Vasectomies *can* be reversed—*sometimes.* Although major surgery is involved, microsurgical vasovasotomy (reconnecting the tubes) is the technique used when remarriage or another major life change makes a man decide to father children again. Some doctors claim a 40–50% success rate on vasectomy reversals (provided the wife is fertile, of course). This figure will probably rise as microsurgical techniques continue to become more sophisticated.

More information: Association for Voluntary Sterilization, 708 Third Ave., New York 10017.

Headache Relief Without Drugs

Relief from incapacitating tension, vascular and migraine headaches is possible without drugs, using a self-administered form of acupuncture known as *acupressure.*

The technique: Exert *very heavy* thumbnail pressure (painful pressure) successively on nerves lying just below the surface of the skin at key points in the hands and wrists. As with acupuncture, no one's sure *why* it works.

Pressure points to try:

• The triangle of flesh between the thumb and index finger on the back of your hands (thumb side of bone, near middle of the second metacarpal in the index finger).

• Just above the protruding bone on the thumb side of your wrist.

Getting a Good Night's Sleep Without Pills

Sleep problems—from real insomnia to occasional restless slumber—can be cured.

The first step in the cure is to become aware that you're not alone—and that something can be done.

Occasional insomniacs usually contribute to their problem by worrying that theirs is a serious problem—and a symptom of even more sleep problems in the future. Occasional means anything from one sleepless night a week to one a year. In most cases, sufferers should dismiss those symptoms. They are usually caused by some specific and temporary stress or anxiety.

How do you know when your *occasional* insomnia has become a *chronic* disorder?

To be a chronic problem, the loss of sleep must have a real effect on your *daytime* functioning. A good question to ask yourself is, "What would I be doing differently during the day if I were getting eight hours sleep at night?" In other words, what benefit would being able to sleep bring you?

Sometimes, a person is simply not sleeping as much as he *thinks* he should, but his daytime functioning is not adversely affected. In those cases, the individual probably is trying to sleep more hours than he needs to.

Prescription for the occasional insomniac: Condition your sleep environment. Learn to associate your bed and your bedroom with sleep.

How to do it?:

• Pay attention to bedroom conditions, such as light, heat, noise. Shut off telephones if necessary. Keep temperature cool (around 68°). Make sure your mattress and your sleep clothing are comfortable.

• If you don't fall asleep right away, get up, leave the bedroom, and go do something else. Don't lie awake thinking about it. Staying in bed for hours trying to get to sleep accentuates the problem. You begin to associate your bed and bedroom with *try-*

ing to sleep instead of with sleeping.

• Stick to a regular bedtime schedule. Go to bed at the same time every night—weekdays and weekends. Some insomniacs have the idea they'll catch up on missed sleep on the weekends. You can't do it. Trying to do it simply disrupts your biological rhythms.

Other popular sleep inducers or aids:

• Sleeping pills. Doctor-prescribed sedatives are very useful in *temporary* situations where a particular emotional or physical upset is the cause of the insomnia. *Problem:* Tendency to become dependent on them, and a worsening of the quality of sleep as more pills are used.

How to handle pills: Use for no more than a week or two. Expect that sleep will be very disturbed on the first night or two after stopping the pills. That's perfectly normal. Expect it and accept it.

• Nonprescription, over-the-counter sleeping pills are absolutely useless. Studies have shown "sugar pills" to be just as effective.

• *Exercise.* Early in the day is okay. Late in the evening is too stimulating.

Exception to the rule: Sexual activity, within a comfortable relationship where no tension or anxiety exists, is helpful.

• *Caffeine.* Coffee, tea, soft drinks act as stimulants. Avoid completely.

• *Alcohol.* May help you get to sleep but interferes with quality of sleep. Wears off after several hours.

• Widely advertised insomnia cures like vibrating beds, prerecorded cassette tapes, sleep masks are fine if they relax you.

Source: Dr. Frank Zorick, former clinical director of the sleep disorder center at Cincinnati Veterans Administration Hospital and the University of Cincinnati.

Facts and Fallacies About Dental Care

• Bad teeth *don't* cause headaches, bursitis or anything like that. But jaw and tooth pains may be "referred" pains that originate in other areas.

• A tooth knocked out in an accident *can* be saved. When a child falls and loses a tooth, pick it up, don't stop to clean it. Wrap it in a wet cloth, and bring it and the child as quickly as possible to the dentist. Reimplantation works best with children (sometimes works with adults, too).

• Playing the trumpet or trombone can correct a bad bite. However, playing flute or piccolo can make it worse. Saxophone can work either way.

• Pain perception is less in the morning than in the afternoon, according to recent research. *Suggestion:* Schedule dental appointments early in the day.

• If you don't want to pay for a crown for a badly decayed tooth, ask for a filling with reinforcement pins. That does the job almost as well at a fraction of the cost.

• *Toothbrushes.* Use two or more in rotation so that they can dry out properly. *Soft* nylon is best. Natural bristle brushes take longer to dry. If not used properly, they can damage gum tissue because bristles are too firm and coarse. Angled brushes may help in reaching some areas. *Caution:* Too-vigorous brushing can wear grooves in tooth enamel. When used correctly, a toothbrush will not abrade tissues or teeth. And hardness of the bristles is not as significant as *the way the brush is used* and *the time spent brushing.*

• *Dental floss. Unwaxed* floss is better because it absorbs particles.

• *Flushing devices* (such as Water Pik): If used with too much pressure, device can damage tissue, force debris into periodontal pockets, and cause inflammation and infection. *Recommendation:* Use at half the recommended pressure.

Understanding Hospital Talk

A hospital patient may have considerable difficulty understanding some of the jargon used by nurses and other hospital personnel. Here is what some commonly used terms mean:

NPO—Sign placed by the bed of a patient who is not to get anything to eat or drink.

Emesis basin—Basin brought to patients who are sick to their stomach.

Ambulate—Take the patient for a walk.

Force fluids—Encourage intake of lots of liquid.

Void—Urinate.

IV—Intravenous.

OOB—Out of bed.

IPPB—Intermittent Positive Pressure Breathing Machine to aid the breathing.

HS—Medication before sleep.

BP—Blood pressure.

HR—Heart rate.

Medication schedule:

QID—4 times a day.

TID—3 times a day.

BID—2 times a day.

OD or QD—Once a day.

QOD—Every other day.

Questions to Ask a Surgeon

To protect against unnecessary surgery, ask the physician hard questions *beforehand.*

- What are the risks?
- What is the mortality rate for this operation?
- How long will it take to recover?
- What is the likelihood of complications? What sort?
- Are there alternative ways to treat this condition?
- How many people have you seen with similar symptoms who have chosen *not* to have surgery?
- How many of these operations have you done in the past year?

Always get a second opinion.

Preventing Tennis Elbow

Most important factor in preventing tennis elbow is your swing. While pros usually develop the pain on the inside of the elbow (from their service), recreational players get the condition on the outside of the arm (from the backhand).

- *Solution:* Switch to a two-handed stroke. *Also:* Be especially careful not to turn the wrist upward as you come through the backhand stroke. And keep the elbow firm at the time of impact. Other preventives:
- *Racquet:* Metal rather than wood; flexible rather than rigid; light head rather than heavy; as large a handle as is comfortable, perhaps a 4⅝-inch grip if you have a big enough hand. Don't string with nylon; choose 16-gauge gut, and avoid tight stringing—52 or 54 pounds will be the right tension for most amateur players.
- *Balls:* Avoid pressureless balls. Beware of heavier balls, particularly the Italian imports. Be careful if you are vacationing in the mountains about using balls bought for sea-level play; they will bounce faster, forcing you to stroke before you've gotten your body ready.
- *Courts:* A problem only if you switch to a faster court from a slow clay surface that you are used to. Makes you prone to taking the strokes late.

Source: *Physicians & Sportsmedicine.*

Alcohol Without Hangovers

Some hangover discomfort is caused by *congeners* (toxic chemicals formed during fermentation). Vodka has the lowest congener content, gin next. Blended scotch has four times the congener content of gin. Brandy, rum, and pure malt scotch have six times that amount; bourbon eight times.

Retard the absorption of alcohol by eating before and during drinking (especially foods, such as cheeses, containing fatty proteins).

Use water as a mixer. Carbonation speeds the absorption of alcohol.

If you get a hangover anyway, the only known cures are rest, aspirin, and time. Endless roster of other remedies—ranging from cucumber juice and salt to a Bloody Mary—have more to do with drinking mythology than with medical fact, although according to psychologists who have studied hangovers, if you believe in a cure, it may help.

When Blood Pressure Can Fool You

Blood-pressure readings are often deceptively high when taken in a hospital or doctor's office. *Reason:* The patient's system reacts to anxiety over the test or the doctor's presence. In an Italian study, 47 of 48 patients' pressure rose after the doctor appeared. (In one case, the systolic reading went up by 75 points.) *Solution:* When three or four measurements were taken over a period of 10 minutes, the last was likely to be accurate.

Source: *New Scientist,* King's Reach Tower, Stamford St., London SE1 9LS, weekly.

Collecting More on Your Company Health Policy

Health insurance policies are not etched in stone. There are contractual provisions in the insurance policy that are negotiable.

Most companies give health insurance to engender goodwill among employees. Many problems in collecting the maximum due you are a result of incompetence or negligence on the part of the administrators in your company who handle insurance benefits. They may be too busy or unaware of how to get more for you.

Three ways to improve your ability to collect:

- Know the insurance contract and all its provisions. Be aware that everything is negotiable. Example: Home health care by someone other than a registered nurse or practical nurse is not covered in the policy. Contractually nothing needs to be said, but adminstratively an alternate source of home health care could be covered. It is really a question of negotiation.

• Have the company's insurance broker help negotiate with the insurer. He is the one who is making the money from selling your company the policy. He also has more leverage than you do with the insurance company. If he is unwilling to help, encourage your company to switch to a more cooperative broker.

• Set up a liaison. The individual in your company in charge of claims should have a good working relationship with the insurance company. Reason: If the settlement is too low or doesn't fully cover your needs, the claims person at your firm can make a better settlement. After all, the insurance company is selling policies.

Strategy: If your claims person is uncertain whether you can get more compensation for an ailment or treatment, ask for permission to contact the broker. The broker should know the terms of your contract and be familiar with the people at the insurance company. He should have an idea of how to get the claim paid, especially if it's a legitimate claim but a trifle unusual.

Take advantage of situations where both spouses are covered at their jobs by group insurance policies to increase your benefits.

Example: You both have Blue Cross to cover hospitalization and, in addition, you both have major medical. Typically, the major medical has a $100 deductible. The insurance company will pick up 80% of the next $2,000 and 100% thereafter. However, if both spouses coordinate their policies, you could wind up using the other's policy to pay that remaining 20% of the $2,000.

Don't expect to make a profit by having several insurance policies. Years ago many health insurance policies were not coordinated and it was possible to get duplicate payments. Today all plans are coordinated so you can't get duplicate payments.

Trying to make specifically unallowable treatments allowable: This is between the doctor and you. For instance, if you want to claim cosmetic surgery necessary for health reasons, consult your doctor. If he won't go along with it, you are not going to get anywhere with the insurance broker, the personnel at your office, or the insurance company.

If you are stuck with a flawed company policy and find you have huge deductibles and other uncovered expenses, take out a personal policy that coordinates with the company's.

Source: Leonard Stern, president, Leonard B. Stern & Co., an insurance consulting and brokerage firm, 65 E. 55 St., Suite 303, New York 10022.

How to Find a Good Nursing Home

Most families postpone as long as possible the decision to use a nursing home. Once the decision is reached, the process of selecting a good facility is so painful that often they move too fast. *Good advice:* Give parent time to get used to the idea. Meanwhile, investigate every possible choice thoroughly.

How to begin: Get lists of not-for-profit, community-based homes from your church, fraternal order, state agency on aging, American Association of Homes for the Aging (Suite 770, 1050 17th St. NW, Washington, DC 20036), or American Health Care Association (1200 15th St. NW, Washington, DC 20005).

Costs: If parent's resources are small, Medicaid may provide financial support for nursing home care. Homes offering complete care in metropolitan areas usually charge $50–$80 per day (depending on the amount of care required). Some require a large advance gift or admission fee. (Health insurance sometimes covers nursing homes.) Patients paying their own way may be eligible for Medicaid assistance after their savings run out. Check the rules in your state.

Evaluating a Nursing Home

1. Accreditation, license, and certification for Medicare and Medicaid should be current and in force.

2. *Best to arrive without an appointment.* Look at everything. Building and rooms should be clean, attractive, safe, and meet all fire codes. Residents should not be crowded (ask about private rooms; sometimes they're available at reasonable extra cost). Visit dining room at mealtime. Check kitchen, too. Visit activity rooms when in session. Talk to residents to find out how they feel about the home.

3. Staff should be professionally trained and large enough to provide adequate care for all residents.

4. *If home requires a contract, read it carefully.* Show it to your lawyer before signing. Some homes reserve the right to discharge a patient whose condition has deteriorated even if lump-sum payment was made upon admittance. *Best:* An agreement that allows payment by the month, or permits refunds or advance payment if plans change.

5. Find out exactly what services the home provides and which ones cost extra. Private duty nurses are not included. Extras like shampoo, hairset, can be exorbitant. (A box of tissues can cost a dollar.) Make a list of the "extras" your parents will need for a comfortable life. Try to supply some of them yourself.

Before you decide on a home, you and your parent should have a talk with the administrator and department heads. Find out who is in charge of what, and whom to speak to if problems arise.

Source: Sheldon Goldberg, Am. Assn. of Homes for the Aging.

Cordless Phone Alert

Cordless phones have caused partial hearing loss in several users. The problem is that the phone's ringer is located within the earpiece and can ring in the ear at sound levels up to 141 decibels. *Solution:* Don't forget to flip the switch from *standby* to *talk* every time that the phone is answered.

Nonstick Pan Alert

Nonstick pans (such as Teflon or Silverstone) can be dangerous if allowed to boil dry. At 400°F, the pans may release toxic fumes after 20 minutes—enough to make a person sick. *Especially susceptible:* Birds and other pets.

Alternative Medicine: How to Cure a Cold

Recent research has shown that a technique called *Visualization* is effective in curing colds by strengthening the body's immune system.

Basic idea: Every morning and evening for fifteen minutes and every hour for two to five minutes, relax and visualize yourself getting well.

To relax: Slow your breathing (take deeper breaths). Direct your attention inward by following your breath to the center of your body. Enter a peaceful state of picturing a ball of golden light within you. Become that ball of golden light.

To visualize: Keep it simple. See yourself well, with a clear uncongested nose, throat or chest. Imagine the cells in the distressed area of your body being cleaned by luminous white cells.

Source: Barbara A. Brennan, an experienced psychic healer and bioenergetic therapist, is president, Healing Science Institute, 331 E. 71st St., Box 21, New York 10021. The institute offers a four-year training program in healing.

How to Evaluate High-Technology Stocks

High technology is the last frontier in American business. Although these stocks have declined sharply during bear markets, they have outperformed other stocks, rebounding more sharply in subsequent recoveries.

Smaller companies developing new technologies, or making a breakthrough on an old one, have three things going for them. These advantages:

Since they are small, the impact on their earnings from the new product or system can be significant.

They are generally free from government regulation because their earnings are often in a new field (except in the case of medicine, where the Food and Drug Administration reigns supreme).

If the company scores a significant breakthrough, it has a chance to dominate a growing market. That's an extremely profitable position even if the market served is relatively small.

Rules for the budding high-technology investor:

Invest in a technology company only if you perceive it as serving a current social need. Some technologies are ahead of their time and are initially rejected. Example: When cable TV was introduced in the 1960s, it attracted hordes of investors but few subscribers. Today, there is a definite subscriber demand and cable TV is a far more attractive investment.

The high-technology expertise of the proposed company must be a meaningful part of the firm's business. For instance, the largest contractor in electronic warfare is General Telephone and Electronics Corp. However, that technology accounts for a mere 1% of its earnings. But the number four in the field, Sanders Associates, gets most of its income from its electronic warfare technology. Point: Large firms don't always have the edge on high technology or research.

No matter how attractive a scientific breakthrough may seem, don't buy a company operating at a deficit. Business graveyards are loaded with firms that couldn't deliver because of their poor financial situation. Following this rule may force you to pay a little more for your stock, but it will eliminate a good deal of the risk.

Ignore the market indexes: Companies with technological superiority are not tied to a stock market environment over time.

Keep current on technological innovation. Read scientific papers, magazines and investment guides that deal with technology.

Source: Louis Ehrenkrantz, vice president, Rosenkrantz, Ehrenkrantz, Lyon and Ross, Inc., investment bankers, 6 E. 43 St., New York 10017, and author of *Growth Investing and Technology.*

Spotting Low-Priced Stocks Ready to Bounce Back

The key to success in the stock market is knowing how to recognize value. Here is the successful approach of Robert Ravitz, director of research at the investment management firm David J. Greene & Co.

At the Greene operation, value has little to do with a good company versus a bad company. A top-quality large company selling at a high price/earnings multiple is less attractive than a lesser-quality company selling at a depressed price in terms of its past and future earning power, working capital, book value and historical prices.

Here is where Greene's analysts look for value:

Stocks that have just made a new low for the last 12 months.

Companies that are likely to be liquidated. In the process of liquidation, shareholders may get paid considerably more than the stock is selling for now.

Unsuccessful merger candidates. If one buyer thinks a company's stock is a good value, it's possible that others may also come to the same conclusion.

Companies that have just reduced or eliminated their dividends. The stock is usually hit with a selling wave, which often creates a good buying opportunity.

Financially troubled companies in which another major company has a sizable ownership position. If the financial stake is large enough, you can be sure that the major company will do everything it can to turn the earnings around and get the stock price up so that its investment will work out.

Opportunities, also, in stocks that are totally washed out—that is, situations where all the bad news is out. The stock usually has nowhere to go but up. How to be sure a stock is truly washed out:

Trading volume slows to practically nothing. If over-the-counter, few if any dealers making a market.

No Wall Street research analysts are following the company any more.

No financial journalists, stock market newsletters, or advisory services discuss the company.

Selling of the stock by company's management and directors has stopped.

Signs of a turnabout:

The company plans to get rid of a losing division or business. If so, be sure to learn whether the company will be able to report a big jump in earnings once the losing operation is sold.

The company is selling off assets to improve its financial situation and/or reduce debt.

A new management comes on board with an established track record of success with turnaround situations.

Management begins buying the company's stock in the open market.

Also, be sure to follow 13d statements filed with the Securities and Exchange Commission (SEC). A company or individual owning 5% or more of a public company must report such holdings to the SEC. If any substantial company is acquiring a major position in a company, it's possible a tender offer at a much higher price is in the wind.

Source: Robert Ravitz, director of research, David J. Greene & Co., an investment management firm, 30 Wall St., New York 10005.

Key Questions to Ask When Selecting a Stockbroker

Be sure that you do the interviewing. Don't let the prospective broker turn the tables and interview you. Here are some key areas to cover when interviewing a potential stockbroker:

- Where did he study? What?
- How long has he been with the brokerage firm? How long has he been in the securities industry? What was his prior employment? Why did he leave his last place of employment?
- From where does he get his investment recommendations? His firm's research department? Company contacts? Friends in the business? His own research? A combination?
- Can he supply a certified history of his firm's and his own research recommendations?
- Does he have any client references?
- What is his theory on giving sell advice and profit taking?
- How many clients does the account executive service? (You want your telephone calls to be answered promptly.)
- How diversified is the brokerage firm? Does it have, for example, a bond department? How about an economist? An in-house market technician (essential for timing)? Money-market experts? Commodity department? Option department? Tax-shelter experts?
- How many industries does the firm's research department follow? How many companies? How many senior analysts does the firm have?
- Will you be getting weekly, monthly, or only occasional printed research reports?
- What fees, if any, will be charged for such services as securities safekeeping?
- What is the firm's commission structure? What discounts is it willing to offer?
- Can the investor talk directly to the investment-research analyst to get firsthand clarifications and updates on research reports? Must everything be funneled through the account executive?
- What is the financial condition of the brokerage firm? (You want the latest annual and quarterly financial statements.)
- How many floor brokers does the firm have at the various stock exchanges? (You want prompt order execution.)
- Is the potential broker willing to meet personally on a regular basis (monthly or quarterly, depending on portfolio size and activity) to discuss progress?
- What kind of monthly customer statements are prepared? (More and more firms now offer tabulation of monthly dividend income, portfolio valuation and annual portfolio yield estimate.)

The Scandalous Wall Street "Specials"

One of the more insidious stockbroker-dealer practices is the use of "specials" to dispose of inventory. When a brokerage firm wants to dump an over-the-counter (unlisted) security that it has in its own inventory, it substantially increases the commission it pays to its account executives if they sell it promptly.

Since the security comes out of the firm's inventory, the transaction is called a principal transaction. These are generally done on a net basis. On the confirmation slip that the customer receives, there is no breakdown between the actual price of the security and the commission charged. *Result:* The customer doesn't really know the exact commission or the stock's precise price. This obfuscation allows the broker to charge a higher price for the security than may be dictated by supply and demand. As a result of this ploy, the firm can afford to give its account executives the higher commissions.

Why is the account executive so eager to sell you a particular security? Does it really fit into your investment program? Does he have a research report recommending it?

There are two main reasons why brokers want to unload stocks in their inventory. They have become disenchanted with the stock's prospects, or the carrying (interest) charges have become excessive. Some firms announce "specials" to the account executives on an almost daily basis.

Safeguard: One of the most important safeguards any investor should employ is to ask his account executive for a research report on any recommendation that is made, even if it is only a brief one.

Confirmation slips should indicate when a brokerage firm is selling stock out of its own inventory by stating that it is a principal transaction. Some brokers, however, merely indicate that the transaction was done on a net basis and that the firm is a "market maker." An investor who sees these terms may have been an unwitting purchaser of a "special" that was sold to him only because his account executive was eager to get a higher commission. In order to mislead clients, some brokerage firms merely put a small code number on the front of the confirmation slip. On the back of that slip, in tiny print, one can find that the code number means that, in fact, a principal transaction was done.

Bottom line: Instruct your broker to always inform you beforehand whether the transaction is likely to be a principal or an agency transaction, which means that the broker is acting as a middleman or on behalf of another investor. Confirmation slips for agency transactions should state separate price and commission charges.

How to Earn Interest in Two Money Market Funds on the Same Money

Squeeze out a little bit more income by playing the float.

Switch money from one fund to another. Although deposits are credited almost immediately, it takes a few days for money-fund checks to clear. That means an investor can legally earn daily interest in two places from the same money.

One Florida resident keeps $10,000 in five different funds. Each month he mails a $5,000 check from one fund to another, trying to ensure that his deposits arrive on a Thursday. He is credited by Friday, but that money won't come out of his other fund until Tuesday. Meanwhile, for five days he appears to have $15,000 in each account.

There are variations on this strategy, like switching money from NOW accounts into money-market funds. If the NOW account is in a savings and loan institution (these are outside the Federal Reserve System), it takes even longer for that deposit to clear. Other investors have used money-fund checks to buy Treasury bills. Again, they earn double interest for a few days.

Floating between funds may seem like more of a headache than it's worth. Still, there are simple ways to maximize your money-market dividends, like paying all bills, including the IRS's, with money-fund checks.

Funds require a $500 minimum on withdrawals. If your total monthly expenses add up to only $500, write checks from your regular checking account to Con Edison and Ma Bell, and then transfer money from your fund at the last possible moment to cover those disbursements. It's foolish to keep much in a checking account these days.

Some funds seem to be encouraging investors to play the float by offering check-writing privileges on distant banks. Sending checks drawn from West Coast banks to East Coast creditors is nothing new. Businesses have been doing so for many years. Now consumers can play the same game and earn interest into the bargain.

When to Sell a Stock

It's very difficult to know when to sell a stock. Very little research has been done on the subject, and advice from brokers is usually vague and confusing. *Typical comments:* "Let's watch it one more day." "Can't sell it now, but you should get out on the next rally." "It's not doing well right now, but it's sure to come back over the long haul." If the stock you've bought has gone up, the two conflicting clichés on Wall Street are: "Can't get hurt taking a profit," and "Let your profits run."

What to do instead: When it comes to evaluating an individual stock, you should look for one thing—failure. This sounds austere, but what to look for is very specific: A stock that tries to rally and fails to make a new high.

How to identify failure: The stock must sell *below* the price level at which it had held in a previous "correction" (decline). If you were to look at this sequence visually, on a stock chart, you would see a series of lower highs and lower lows. That type of action establishes failure. It defines the stock's trend as down, not up.

Sell! Put aside all hopes that the stock will stabilize or rally wildly or that it will come back if you hold it long enough. The market is telling you, in no uncertain terms, that something is wrong. You don't have to know what or why. That information frequently doesn't come out until the stock has tumbled a very long distance down. You've made an objective decision. Stick with it.

When to decide to sell: When the stock market is closed. That way, each little gyration won't emotionally affect your decision.

After you've made an objective decision, use a protective stop order. *How it works:* Tell your broker to sell the stock automatically when it drops below a certain point.

You can use stop orders effectively, even if the stock rises. Each time the price advances, cancel the old stop order and enter a new one. *One arbitrary rule:* Set the stop order price at 10% below the current market price.

Source: *When to Sell*, by Justin Mamis and Robert Mamis, Farrar, Straus & Giroux, 19 Union Sq. West, New York 10003.

How Options Traders Make Money in a Declining Market

Now that trading in listed *puts* is available on five option exchanges, it's time to see how to use them.

*Puts** provide a way of selling stock short in hope of a market decline, without the risk of severe loss usually associated with short selling.

How puts *work:* Suppose XYZ Corp. is selling at $50 and you can purchase a January-50 *put* on the options exchange for $350. The *put* entitles you to sell 100 shares of XYZ at 50 until the expiration of that option.

If XYZ were to decline to, say, 40, an option carrying the right to sell the shares at 50 would be worth $1,000 (the $10 difference times 100 shares). The profit would accrue immediately to the option holder, who could exercise the option on shares that he could purchase on the open market at 40. Even better, since the commissions would be lower, he could simply sell the option for $1,000. Since he paid $350, his gain would be $650, or 186% on a stock that declined by 20%.

Of course, if XYZ rose or stood still through the life of the option, the option would expire. This would result in a 100% loss. However, the maximum risk to the short-seller using the *put* would be $350, the cost of the option.

Straddles: More Flexibility

The availability of listed *puts*, used with *call*† options, provides some interesting opportunities for mathematically oriented investors. Straddles (using *puts* and *calls*) *can produce profit regardless of the direction of market movement, provided that the underlying common moves away* from its starting price by a certain amount.

Example: Assume XYZ at 50 again, the listed *put* selling for $350 (3½) and the listed January *call*, which entitles the option holder to *buy 100* shares at 50, also selling at 3½. Instead of purchasing the *put* alone, you purchase *both*. Here are the workouts at different prices of XYZ when both options expire on a given date.

Price XYZ	Put Value	Gain (Loss)	Call Value	Gain (Loss)	Net
70	0	− 350	20	+1650	+1300
65	0	− 350	15	+1150	+ 800
60	0	− 350	10	+ 650	+ 300
55	0	− 350	5	+ 150	− 200
50	0	− 350	0	− 350	− 700
45	5	+ 150	0	− 350	− 200
40	10	+ 650	0	− 350	+ 300
35	15	+1150	0	− 350	+ 800
30	20	+1650	0	− 350	+1300

The position shows a profit as long as XYZ moves beyond the 43–57 price range, a 14% movement in either direction from the starting price of 50.

It's possible to profit on both sides of a straddle. *Example:* If XYZ first rises to 60 and then falls to 40, you might sell or exercise your *call at a profit in the rise and then sell or exercise your put* for an additional profit in the fall. However, in practice, one side or the other of a straddle is usually exercised, not both.

Straddles are best purchased after the market has rested within a trading range for some time and you expect a breakout but are uncertain of the direction. And, of course, you should purchase an option only when option premiums (the price of options) are running below normal.

**Put:* The right to *sell* shares of a specified stock at a specified price until a specified date.

†*Call:* The right to *buy* a specified stock at a specified price until a specified date.

"Creative" Accounting That Conceals Corporate Problems From Potential Investors

• Delaying the publication of financial results as long as legally possible.

• Capitalization of research costs, basing the write-offs against existing or expected orders.

• Continuation of dividend payments from *new equity or loans.*

• Cuts in routine maintenance until repairs are so overdue that it's necessary to renovate.

• Considering leasing agreements as *capital* rather than as what they are—*loans.*

• Dividend increases from subsidiaries to the parent company and consolidation of more and more subsidiary results, from wholly and partially owned subsidiaries, into the parent company financial statements.

• Retention of the main asset of the business in the owner's name (or that of the owner's spouse) rather than the company name (thereby removing it as a source of payment to creditors).

• The valuation of assets at whatever figure is wanted, since nobody may notice.

• Capitalizing interest charges, training expenses, computer *installation* costs.

• Using inflation as a cloud to hide assets revaluation.

• Paying company debts out of the proprietor's pocket to improve profits before he sells his shares.

• Inventory valuation at latest market *selling* price rather than at actual cost.

• Deferral of current expense to next year to improve this year's sales and profits.

• Inadequate provision for depreciation by failing to revalue assets.

Source: *Corporate Collapse*, by John Argenti, John Wiley & Sons, 605 Third Ave., New York 10016.

Making Profits on a Stock Split

When a stock splits, the average profit to an investor is 20%. But the greatest profits are generally made in three to six months before the split is announced. The general pattern is that the price stays high for two days after the split announcement and then declines. To spot a candidate for a split, look for:

• A company that needs to attract more stockholders, diversify or attract additional financing.

• A takeover candidate (heavy in cash and liquid assets) whose management holds only a small percentage of the outstanding shares. (Companies with concentrated ownership rarely split stock unless there are problems with taxes, acquisitions or diversification.)

• A stock priced above $75. A split moves it into the more attractive $25–$50 range.

• A stock that was split previously and price has climbed steadily since then.

• Earnings prospects so strong that the company will be able to increase dividends after the split.

Likely prospects are over-the-counter companies with current earnings of $2.5 million, at least $2 million annually in preceding years and less than 1 million shares outstanding (or under 2,000 shareholders). A stock split is necessary if management wants to list on a major exchange.

Source: C. Colburn Hardy, *Dun & Bradstreet's Guide to Investments,* Thomas Y. Crowell Co., New York.

Techniques for Evaluating Over-the-Counter Stocks

Growth potential is the single most important consideration. Earnings increase should average 10% over the past six years when acquisitions and divestitures are factored out. Cash, investments, accounts receivable, materials and inventories should be twice the size of financial claims due within the next year.

In addition, working capital per share should be greater than the market value of the stock (an $8 stock should be backed by $10 per share in working capital). Long-term debt should be covered by working capital, cash or one year's income. And the balance sheet should show no deferred operating expenses and no unreceived income.

The criteria for final selections include ownership by at least 10 institutions reported in *Standard & Poor's Stock Guide* and public ownership of between 500,000 and one million shares, with no more than 10% controlled by a single institution. There should also be continued price increases after a dividend or split, and a strong likelihood of moving up to a major exchange. (A good sign is strong broker and institutional support.)

OTC stocks to avoid are those of companies expanding into unrelated fields, where they lack the required management experience and depth, and stocks selling at prices far below recent highs. This sign of loss of investor support can take months to overcome.

Source: C. Colburn Hardy, *Physician's Management,* New York.

What to Watch Besides the Dow

Too many investors rely exclusively on the Dow Jones industrial average for a quick view of what the market is doing. But the Dow reflects only stock price changes of 30 large, mature companies. Their performance does not necessarily reflect the market as a whole. The Dow should be supplemented with these indexes:

The over-the-counter composite index gauges the cumulative performance of over-the-counter issues. It points to a bull market when it outpaces the Dow Jones industrial average and to a bear market when it is weaker.

TRIN, an acronym for the trading index, measures the relative volume of rising and declining issues. The market is bullish when the TRIN falls from a reading of above 1.20 to below .70 during one day of trading. It is bearish when the TRIN goes from below .70 to 1.20. A reading of 1.00 shows an even relationship between advancing and declining stocks.

The Quotron change, named for the company that developed it, measures the daily percentage change for all issues on the New York Stock Exchange (the QCHA index) and the American Stock Exchange (QACH). It gives an excellent picture of what the market is doing in broad terms. Mutual funds track more closely with the Quotron change than the Dow Jones industrial average.

The Dow Jones transportation average is a generally reliable lead indicator of intermediate trends. The Dow Jones utilities average reflects income- and interest-sensitive stocks. It's a good long-term lead indicator.

In a bull market, the total number of shares traded expands on days when advances outpace declines. The opposite occurs in a bear market. A sign of market reversal is a high-volume day when the market moves in one direction all morning, then turns around.

A Guide to Market Indicators

- *The speculation index.* Divide the weekly trading volume on the American Stock Exchange (in thousands) by the number of issues traded. Calculate the same ratio for New York Stock Exchange trading. Divide the AMEX ratio by the NYSE ratio to calculate the speculation index. Strategists believe the market is bearish when the index is more than .38 (and especially so if it rises to .38 and then falls back). Less than .20 is bullish.
- *Member short selling.* Divide the number of shares NYSE members sell short each week by total NYSE short selling. The index is bearish when readings of .87 are reached. A reading below .75 is very bullish, particularly if it lasts several weeks.
- *New highs—new lows.* The market is usually approaching an intermediate bottom when the number of new lows reaches 600. The probable sign of an intermediate top is 600 new highs in one week, followed by a decline in number the next week.
- *The NYSE short-interest ratio.* The total number of outstanding shares sold short each month divided by the average daily trading volume for that month. A strong rally generally comes after the ratio reaches 1.75.
- *The 10-week moving NYSE average.* Compute the average NYSE index for the previous 10 weeks, then measure the difference between last week's close and the average. When the gap between the last weekly close and the 10-week average remains at 4.0 or below for two to three weeks, investors can expect an intermediate advance. Market tops are usually near when the last week's index is 4.0 or more above the previous 10-week average.

Only once or twice a year will as many as four of the five indicators signal an intermediate bottom. But when four do, it is highly reliable. The same is true for intermediate tops.

Source: *Barron's,* New York, and *Indicator Digest,* Palisades Park, N.J.

Travel

New Tricks for the Shrewd Traveler

Getting the seat you prefer on an airplane has become increasingly difficult. Reaching the airport at a reasonable time before takeoff used to ensure a decent seat. But this is no longer the case, now that airlines preassign a seat when a reservation is made.

Best Strategies

If you're assigned to a seat you don't like, go back to the desk when all the prereserved seats are released (usually 15 minutes before flight time). All the prime seats for passengers who didn't show up are available then.

If on the plane you discover that you don't like your seat, don't wait until the plane takes off to find a better one. Look around the plane, and the second before they close the door head for the empty seat of your choice. Don't wait until the seat-belt sign goes on.

By prereserving a single seat on a nonjumbo where the seats are three across, you'll increase the odds of getting an empty seat next to you. Ask for a window or aisle seat in a row where the window or aisle is already reserved by a *single.* The middle seat between two singles is least likely to fill up. *Desperation measure:* Say you're very overweight and need an empty seat next to you so you won't crowd the other passengers.

Flight Tactics

There are other factors that every shrewd traveler should know:

- If you carry a hanging bag on the plane and put it in one of those little front closets, someone else can easily take it by mistake. Those bags all look alike. *Be aware:* Luggage you carry onto the plane *is not insured* against such mishaps. *Remedy:* Tie a bright-colored ribbon or string around the handle. A name tag isn't enough. If someone else picks up your bag, the ribbon should alert him to his mistake.

- If you change your reservation to a different flight and your ticket must be changed, don't wait in the long line at the airline's front desk. As long as your destination remains the same, you can take your ticket directly to the gate and change it there—even if you've switched airlines or fares. The desk at the gate has a charge card imprinter to deal with any changes. *Added advantage:* You won't miss your flight by waiting in line if you're already at the gate.

- If you've rented a car and don't want to drag your bags on and off the rental agency's airport bus, drop your bags off *first* at the curbside check-in and *then* return the car. *Tip the curbside checker.* You don't want your luggage to be "accidentally" misrouted. Advise the attending porter.

Handling Hotels

When you arrive at the hotel, check your bags. Then go to the pay telephone in the lobby and call the hotel. Ask to have your reservation confirmed, give them your charge card number and go on your way. *Reason:* You'll sidestep convention check-in lines.

To avoid the long line after the convention, go down to the desk very early in the morning, before official checkout time, and check out. You won't have to turn in your room key, and you can still use your room until official checkout time (usually around 1 P.M.).

Don't stay glued to your hotel room if you're waiting for a call. If notified, the hotel operator will transfer your calls to another room, interrupt the call you're on for a more important one or hold any calls while you run out for a soda.

Save money by not paying for things you didn't order. Don't charge anything to your hotel room. It's too confusing when you're checking out to verify the list of room charges. And it's only too easy for the hotel to make a mistake. Most travelers just sign and pay without looking at the list. If you don't charge anything at all, you'll know that extra items on your bill *can't* be yours. *How to do it:* Pay cash for room service, laundry, etc. Use your credit card for food.

And don't depend only on the hotel for information. If you need a service in a strange city (typing, film developing, etc.), call the local convention bureau. It's specifically set up to help out-of-town businesspeople, and every city has one.

Source: Dr. Barbara A. Pletcher, executive director of the National Association for Professional Saleswomen, Box 255708, Sacramento, CA 95865. She's the author of *Travel Sense,* ACE Books, 51 Madison Ave., New York 10010.

What the Airlines Don't Tell You

- Never accept the first fare quoted. Half the time, some other airline's flight within hours of the one you booked has a special, less expensive deal.

- Take advantage of "illegal" connections. These are connecting flights usually less than 45 minutes apart—too close for airlines to feel safe in making them connect. *Result:* These flights usually do not even show up on the computer when your trip is being routed. *Way out:* Have your agent write up your flight in two separate tickets. The second is for the illegal connection that originates at your transfer point.

Example: You arrive at O'Hare in Chicago on the way to San Francisco. Instead of waiting three hours for the safe connecting flight, you already have a separate ticket from O'Hare to San Francisco on an illegal connection. If you miss the connection, you turn that ticket in for the next available flight. *Cost for two separate tickets:* No more than one through ticket. *Baggage:* Waiting for it to be unloaded can cost you valuable time on this tight schedule. *Best:* Travel with carry-on luggage.

• Some supersaver fares are low enough that even if you can't stay as long as their requirements (usually seven days), you will save by buying *two* round-trip tickets—one from your home to your destination for the day you want to leave and one from your destination to your home for the day you want to return. The total may be less than the regular round-trip fare.

• If you miss your flight and there's just time to catch another, go right to the other airline's departure gate instead of to its ticket counter. If it has an empty seat, the second airline will usually honor the ticket for the flight you missed.

• Best seat in the plane. After first class, the choices center on your priorities. For comfort and a smooth ride, pick a seat over the wings. For silence, sit as far forward as possible, but avoid the galley and rest rooms. For leg room, try the first row or seats beside the emergency exits.

• Best way to get standby seat. Reserve a coach seat for your flight. Arrive at the airport the day you are to leave and see if you can get a standby ticket (Monday, Tuesday and Wednesday *are the best standby days*). If you do get a standby seat, become a noshow on your reservation (it's built into the price of your ticket) for a full refund. You may win. You can't lose.

Source: *Your Money and Your Life* by Robert Z. Aliber, Basic Books, 10 E. 53 St., New York 10022.

In-Flight Photos

Get a window seat on the shaded side of the plane, up front (clear of wing and distorting engine exhaust). Don't hold the camera against the window (vibrations will cause blur), and don't angle it (glass reflects).

Use a shutter speed of at least 1/250 and a filter that minimizes blue-sky haze to sharpen scenes on the ground. Warning: Since some countries ban in-flight photos, inquire before takeoff.

Traveler Beware

• *Don't fly within 12 hours after dental work.* The change in atmospheric pressure can cause severe pain.

• *First-class air travel.* Not worth the 30% premium unless the flight lasts more than four hours.

• *You shouldn't pay the 8% federal tax on airfare* if you're flying from one US city to another US city in order to catch a flight to another country. You may have to show the agent the foreign ticket.

• *Carry your medical history.* Fold a one-page summary of health data into your passport. What it should include: Blood type, allergies, eyeglass prescription, medications currently being taken, any preexisting health condition.

• *Don't buy travel insurance at airports.* Coverage is much more expensive and rates vary from city to city. Better: Buy directly from insurance company.

• *Confirm airline reservations when the small box in the center of the airline ticket is marked "RO."* It indicates that the travel agent has only requested a seat, and wait-listing status is a possibility. A confirmed reservation is indicated by an "OK" on your ticket.

• *Avoid consuming all the food and drink* offered on airplanes. Alcohol, nuts, soft drinks, and other foods that have empty calories can cause a swing from high to low blood sugar. You go from feeling great to feeling tired, cramped, and headachy.

• *Alcohol has more punch during an airplane flight than on the ground.* Reason: Body fluids evaporate quickly in the pressurized dry cabin. And, under pressure, the alcohol absorbs more fluids in the intestinal tract, thus making itself felt more quickly. Alternative: To reduce the dehydration of a long flight (six hours or more), drink three or four pints of water.

• *Nonsmoking travelers.* If the airline's check-in clerk says the nonsmoking section is filled, be insistent. The airline must supply nonsmoking seats to all passengers who request to be put in that section.

How to Avoid Jet Lag

• Don't change your watch or habits for brief stops.

• Stay at an airport hotel with 24-hour food service and a quiet room.

• Schedule meetings soon after you arrive if you get there before the end of your normal working day. *Example:* An executive regularly flew from California at 8 A.M. to the East Coast, arriving at 5 P.M. New York time. He knew from experience that he'd have problems "getting started" the next morning, so he scheduled his meeting at 6 P.M., just after he arrived, since it was only 3 o'clock for him.

• For longer stays, be fully rested before departure. Don't rush to the airport. Plan arrivals as close as possible to your normal time for going to sleep. Don't take pills or alcoholic beverages. They hinder the deep sleep vital to recharging mentally.

• Don't plan important hard work for the first or second day of a long trip.

• When traveling, wear comfortable, loose clothing and shoes. *Exercise during the flight.* Isometrics, etc. Don't overeat or drink heavily.

• *Important tip:* If crucial work must be done immediately after arrival, *precondition* your mind and body to the destination's time zone for several days before the trip.

Preventing Montezuma's Revenge

University of Texas Medical School researchers have discovered that the primary ingredient in Pepto-Bismol (bismuth subsalicylate) can help to prevent the most common traveler's ailment. A group of new students in Mexico received four tablespoons of the medication fours times a day (for 21 days.) Others were given a placebo. Diarrhea developed in 14 of 62 students on medication versus 40 of 66 students on the placebo.

Quick Way to Check Hotel Bills

Adjust the amount of the tips so every item that's added to the bill ends with the same digit. Example: Tip odd amounts to have the bills for all meals end in the numeral six. It takes only a moment to skim the list for items that don't end in six, and thus, don't belong on your bill. The odds of an accidental six occurring on the bill are nine-to-one in favor of the traveler.

Outwitting Hotel Thieves

• Don't use a "pickproof" lock in hotel room drawers. That lets the burglar know precisely where your valuables are.

Good place to hide things in hotel room: Under the rug, under the bed. If it's difficult for you to get to, it will also be difficult for burglar.

• Don't drop off your room key at the desk while you're away—until you check out.

• Request duplicate room key.

• When you go out leave a light and the TV on in the room.

• Whenever you leave your car, lock it and take your valuables with you. If parking in a garage that has an attendant, don't leave the key for the trunk.

• Don't put all your cash or traveler's checks in one place or one pocket. Having traveler's checks replaced involves inconvenience.

Duty-Free Shops

Check the prices at duty-free shops against prices in local stores. The airport and dockside shops generally charge higher, rather than prevailing, prices for their products. In addition, top-of-the-line products are sold, meaning that the prices are high to begin with.

So buy only heavily taxed items in these stores. Liquor, cigarettes, perfume and some wines may still be bargains.

Source: *Travel Smart*, 40 Beechdale Rd., Dobbs Ferry, NY 10522, monthly.

Money Abroad

Credit cards are now better than traveler's checks for most trips overseas. Aside from the cards' convenience, they save as much as 6% on exchange costs. *Best bet:* VISA, with a conversion markup only one-quarter of 1% above the wholesale bank currency rate. Other major cards carry a 1% markup—still far better than the 3% or more you'd pay for retail markups on traveler's checks.

Exception: Poorer European countries such as Spain and Third World countries, where dollar-hungry bankers often give a break on traveler's checks or cash.

To change dollars into foreign currency, use banks, not hotels or shops. You'll get a better rate.

Basic Businessman's Wardrobe for a Lengthy Trip

The goal is to travel with only one carry-on garment bag plus one carry-on underseat case, with enough room to add new purchases. Here's a list for up to a month away.

- Lightweight black gabardine suit. Works as business suit and for formal wear.
- Blue blazer for business meetings and evening parties (with gray flannel slacks) or for casual occasions (with blue jeans).
- Pair gray worsted flannel trousers.
- Pair blue jeans.
- Two white broadcloth shirts, plain collar.
- White cotton-knit polo shirt.
- Gray cashmere V-neck sweater, long-sleeved.
- Black-white-and-gray-patterned silk tie.
- Solid maroon silk tie.
- Black silk evening bow tie.
- Five pairs black socks (silk, wool and cotton).
- Five sets of underwear.
- Pair pajamas or one bathrobe.
- Lightweight racing trunks.
- Black plain oxford shoes.
- Black slip-on loafers.
- Tan poplin raincoat with detachable lining (should be worn or carried over arm when boarding plane).

Source: Egon von Furstenberg, *The Power Look*, Holt, Rinehart & Winston, New York.

Holding Down Phone Bills While Traveling In US

Resist the temptation to use credit cards to charge telephone calls. They can increase the price of a call by as much as 500% over the direct-dial method. One reason is that the initial charge on a credit card is three minutes, not one minute.

Develop the habit of calling WATS information at (800) 555-1212 before phoning a hotel, airline or other large service company. Information knows if a company has a free 800 number.

Take advantage of free local calls that can be made from many VIP lounges at major airports.

Don't charge in-state calls to a hotel room. A hotel usually adds a service charge to them, which it cannot legally add to interstate calls. Overseas, use public telephones or arrange to have calls made *to* you from the US. Hotel surcharges from hotels are enormous. In an emergency, call the US and have the person you're trying to reach call you right back.

Pros and Cons of Group Travel Tours

Best reason to choose a package tour: Economy. Saving can amount to several hundred dollars per couple. Food and drink on chartered jets tends to be better than on commercial flights, but space is more cramped. Chartered air-conditioned buses between airports and train stations are a big convenience and eliminate need for constant tipping in foreign currency. *Warning: Chartered deluxe European express trains* are pleasant, but by no means *express.* They are frequently sidetracked for the *real* express trains.

Tours also save time on planning and organizing and are especially helpful to those who have not traveled to a country before or do not speak the language.

Minuses for package tours: Rushed sightseeing schedule. Be wary of promises of *full American breakfasts.* They're usually poor quality. Probably better to stick with a traditional roll and coffee in Europe.

Tip: Save coupon books for gourmet dinners at restaurants on special nights. Pay cash for light suppers when you're tired or have had a late lunch.

Best tour to pick: One sponsored by a local professional, cultural, or educational group. Usually assures you of finding compatible companions.

Choosing a Vacation Cruise

Focus on a cruise with a compatible group. People over 60 generally take longer cruises. People on summer cruises are usually 15 to 20 years *younger* than those on winter cruises.

Compare capacity of the ship's main lounge to number of passengers. If lounge is relatively small, there will be uncomfortable fast meals and guests will scramble for seats at entertainment performances.

Seasick avoidance: Cabin as close to the center of the ship as possible, on the middle deck, off the main corridor.

Tipping Guide

Restaurant tipping guidelines from restaurateurs Vincent Sardi (of Sardi's) and Tom Margittai (co-owner of the Four Seasons):

- *Waiter:* 15% of the bill (not including tax).
- *Captain:* 5%. *Note:* If diner writes tip on the check, the *waiter gets it all,* unless the diner specifies how it is to be split. *(Example:* Waiter, $5; captain ,$2.)
- *Headwaiter who seats diners:* $5 or $10 or more at intervals for regular patrons. He should be tipped in cash.
- *Sommelier:* 10% of the wine selection or 5% if the wine is expensive. $2 or $3 is a good tip.
- *Bartender:* $1 minimum or 15% of check.
- *Hatcheck:* 50 cents to $1 per couple.
- *Restroom attendant:* 50 cents.
- *Doorman* (to get taxi): 50 cents normally. $1 in bad weather or rush hour.
- *Other staff at a restaurant that is regularly used*

should be tipped once or twice a year: Hosts, switchboard operators (where the restaurant provides telephone service).

• *Nightclubs:* Headwaiter should get $2 to $10 per person, depending on the impression the party host wishes to make on his guests. (Higher tip usually ensures better service.)

Other tipping:

• *Limousine service:* 15% to the driver. If service charge is included in bill, tip an additional $5.

• *Hotels:* Valet, room service, bartender should get about 50 cents, depending on amount and quality of service. Bellman: 50 cents per bag. Chambermaid: $1 per day.

• *Sports arenas and racetracks:* A $5 tip to an usher will often give you and your guests access to unused reserved seats.

Tipping Overseas

• *When Leaving the US:* Tip skycaps 25 cents to 50 cents a bag.

• *On a package tour:* Even if tips are "included," employees may not know it, so play it safe. *Bellhops:* 25 cents a bag. *Waiters:* No tip necessary if it's a different one each meal. But if it's the same waiter for the whole stay, a dollar or two on the first day with the promise of the same at the end will usually guarantee top service. *Tour Manager-Guide:* $8 per person per week, $12 for 10 days. *Local guides:* 50 cents per person for a full day.

• *On a cruise:* If employees pool tips (ask the steward), $30 per person per week with an extra 15% of the tab for bartenders, hairdressers and the like. If they don't pool, $1.50 per day for cabin steward and waiter, 75 cents for the busboy. If the ship has a no-tipping policy, $5 to $10 to the waiter at the end of the cruise.

• *Touring on your own:* Depends on the city and country. In Athens, 18 cents to 25 cents (6 to 8 drachmas) each time the doorman hails a cab for you; $2 to $5 a week for the concierge of a hotel; 30 cents per bag for the bellhop, $3 per person per week for the chambermaid.

• *In restaurants:* Usually there's a 15% service charge, so no tip is necessary. But round off the total to the nearest whole currency denomination, as long as it doesn't add more than 5% to the bill.

• *For no tipping at all:* Try Australia, tipping is *not* the custom there, or Iceland, where the 15% service charge covers *all* gratuities.

Best Gambling

Craps and baccarat offer the best shot that Las Vegas casinos give. They take the smallest percentage and are easiest to play. Blackjack is the game for those with a sharp eye and a good memory. *Worst bets:* Keno, roulette and slot machines (in that order). Atlantic City roulette odds are better than Nevada houses but not as good as French casinos. But best blackjack is in Las Vegas, worst in Atlantic City. Best craps rules are in Great Britain.

Insiders' Guide to Casino Gambling

As a weekend gambler, you're basically out for a good time. The odds are you won't break the bank. But you *can* enhance your enjoyment—and maybe even take home some house money—if you follow a few general rules.

• *Go in with a game plan and stick to it.* Decide in advance how much money you're going to take, how much you can afford to lose, and at what point you will quit.

• *Limit each bet to 1% of your original stake.* That may be as little as $5 (the weekend minimum in Atlantic City). Up your bets *only* when you are ahead. Never bet more than 10% of the stake. If you start chasing money you have lost, the odds of going broke are much higher. That's the wrong approach to gambling.

• *Don't push your luck.* If you have won $100 with a given dealer and then lose $20 of your profits, back off. Take a deep breath or break for dinner. In any case, find a new table.

• *Pass up the free drinks.* Casinos offer them for a reason. If you lose your inhibitions, you may desert your strategy and change your betting patterns. You want to keep a clear head.

Blackjack

This is the best casino game—the only one in which a skilled player can beat the house over time. Overall, of course, the casinos make a nice profit because their edge against the average "hunch" player runs from 6% to 15%.

However, with an advanced card-counting system, the odds are turned around. The experienced player has a 2% advantage. Mastery of the counting system takes time and practice. A simplified version gives the player a 15% edge, but it still requires instruction and some dedicated use.

For the recreational gambler, a basic blackjack strategy—with *no* counting—can cut the house edge to only .4%. Given those odds, you'd lose about $2 in an average hour if you bet $4 per hand —not a bad entertainment value.

Rules for the no-count system:

• Never split pairs of 4s, 5s or 10s. Always split aces and 8s. Split other pairs if the dealer's up card is 2 through 6.

• Double your bet on 11 unless the dealer shows an ace. Double on 10 unless the dealer shows an ace or 10. Double on 9 if the dealer shows 3 through 6 and on soft hands (hands with an ace that can be counted as 11 without going over 21) of 13 through 18 if the dealer shows 4 through 6.

- Always stand on hard hands (hands with no ace or an ace that must be counted as 1) of 17 and up. Stand on hands of 12 through 16 if the dealer shows 2 through 6. (Otherwise, hit.) Always stand on soft hands of 18 and up. Always hit on soft hands of 17 or less if it is too late to double.

These rules will keep you out of serious trouble. But human nature being what it is, you will naturally want to play an occasional hunch against the odds. *Best hunch bet:* An "insurance" bet on the dealer's hand when you have been dealt a blackjack. *Reason:* When you have a blackjack, the only thing that can keep you from winning is the dealer also having a blackjack. An insurance bet on his cards assures you of getting at least *something* on the hand.

Craps

This is the most emotional casino game. Fast and noisy, it can sweep you into making more bets per hour than other games—as many as 150. *Result:* The money turns over faster and you lose more. However, if you stick to the most favorable bets, you concede an edge of only .8% to the house.

Bets to make: Pass line. Don't pass. Come. Don't come. In each case, always make the maximum accompanying "odds" bets (these offer the best percentage of all). The only other acceptable wagers are "place" bets on 6 or 8 (the house edge is 1.4% on these).

Avoid all long-shot and one-roll bets like "hardway 4." The stick man will encourage this action because it makes money for the casino. The odds against you are enormous, because the house advantage runs from 10% to 16%.

Under the laws of probability, there is *no* true number system to help the craps gambler. Each roll of the dice is independent. But there are useful betting strategies. *A good one:* After the roller has thrown two passes (winning rolls) up your bet 50% every *other* pass thereafter.

Roulette

Number systems will do you no good in roulette. The general house edge is high: 5.3%. To halve your disadvantage, stick to "outside" even-money bets: Red-black. Odd-even. High-low. If 0 or 00 comes up, you lose only half of these wagers. Other bets are lost in full.

Baccarat

Although the house edge is only 1.1%, this "upper crust" game gives the player no control. *You make only two decisions:* How much you want to put down and whether you choose the banker or the player.

Baccarat players tend to be superstitious, and they are notorious for being streak players.

Warning: The baccarat minimum is generally pretty high—$20–$25. This makes it an expensive game to play.

Slot Machines

Casinos make more than half their profit on slot machines. The house edge is 17%. If you *must* play, find a "progressive" machine that increases its jackpot as money is pumped through it. Some $1 machines pay as high as $250,000.

The ultimate sucker bet is the *big wheel,* a giant circle where numbered sections pay various odds. The house take approaches 25%.

Final Shot

Let's say you've doubled your initial stake, and you have time for one more session before the weekend is over. *Don't be greedy.* Just as you set a strict loss limit (say, 20% of your stake) and stop at it, you should quit while you are ahead, too. Enjoy the sights and the shows, and go home with your profit. If everyone did that, the casinos would be in trouble.

Gambling Trap

Never accept a check to cover a gambling debt. If the check bounces, the amount is not collectible in a court of law. This is true even in states where gambling is legal.

Source: Jerry L. Patterson, director of Jerry Patterson's Blackjack Clinic, 1 Britton Place, Voorhees, NJ 08043, and author of *Casino Gambling,* Perigee Books, 200 Madison Ave., New York 10016.

Security

Protecting Yourself Against Muggers

The best defense against becoming a crime victim is to avoid a setup. Muggers, like most people, don't take more risks or work harder than they have to. Point: They choose victims who seem easy to handle. And they create situations that make the attack simpler.

Chief defense: Don't allow yourself to be distracted, isolated or simply stopped on the street by a stranger. Muggers prefer victims who have stopped moving. They use every technique to accomplish that: Asking for directions, a match or a handout.

First and most important rule: When spoken to by a suspicious stranger, don't stop. Move away quickly. Don't slow down to watch an argument or any other commotion on the street. Fake street fights are a favorite way to set up a robbery.

Defensive tactics: Walk down the sidewalk near the street. Be wary of corners and doorways. Reduce the possibility of being grabbed from the shadows. Hugging the curb permits you to see around the corner while at a distance. Be alert to someone hiding between or behind parked cars.

Walk a couple of extra blocks to take a safe route, especially late at night. Keep to known neighborhoods. Identify in advance where the places of refuge are, in event of trouble.

Look ahead up the street (not down) to see what's happening. Be alert, especially to people loitering or moving suspiciously. Example: Two men up ahead who suddenly separate and begin walking apart. They could be preparing to set you up.

However foolish or rude it may seem, don't get on any self-service elevator if there's somebody at all suspicious on it. Never let an elevator you are on go to the basement. How to avoid it: When entering an open elevator, keep a foot in the door while pressing the floor number. Keep your eyes on the elevator indicator. If the arrow points down, don't get in.

Don't get into a self-service elevator late at night without making sure that nobody is waiting on an upper floor to intercept you. How to do it: Push the top elevator button, but don't get in. If the elevator does not stop on any floor on the way up or down, it's safe.

Avoid places where gangs of juveniles congregate. They can be more dangerous than professional muggers because they will often hurt a victim rather than take the money and run.

Get into the habit of automatically saying excuse me when you bump into someone on the street. Say it no matter whose fault it is.

Never show money in public, whether at a newsstand, market, bank or getting out of a cab. Muggers are watching.

If you are mugged:

Cooperate. Above all, communicate the willingness to cooperate. Keep calm. It can help relax the mugger, too, which is crucial. Reason: If a mugger is pointing a cocked revolver, nervousness on his part could be fatal to you. Ways to calm the situation: Say something reassuring, or ask a distracting question that establishes the mugging as a businesslike transaction. Example: You can have anything you want. Do you mind if I just keep my driver's license?

Never move suddenly. Tell the mugger where your wallet is and ask: Do you want me to get it, or do you want to get it?

A woman mugger with a knife or gun can kill just as easily as a man. Letting macho feelings interfere with cooperating is suicidal.

Don't show the slightest condescension or hostility. Be careful of your tone of voice. Cooperating with disdain can set off violence. Best attitude to project: You've got to earn a living, too. Or: I don't hold this against you at all, times are tough.

Don't make jokes. They are too risky, and the chance for misinterpretation is too great.

Avoid direct or steady eye contact.

If a mugger is particularly hostile, be super-cooperative. Offer money or possessions he has overlooked.

Bottom line: Always carry mugger money. Keep $25 to $100 in your pocket as insurance. A happy mugger is much less likely to do harm than one who comes away empty-handed.

Source: Ken Glickman, director, Seido Self Defense, 61 W. 23rd St., New York 10010.

What a Burglar Thinks About Burglar Alarm Systems

Michael Weaver, in Walla Walla prison, tells what he learned about burglar alarms in his years of dealing with them professionally—*mostly* successfully. *His from-behind-bars report:*

Systems to Avoid

• *Door and window alarms.* They are usually turned on by key when the last person leaves the premises. The alarm systems monitor all the doors and windows. If anyone tries to open them, an alarm sounds. *These systems aren't only worthless, they are an invitation to the burglar. Reason:* They are visible (tape on windows and contact points around doors), so the burglar knows what he has to deal with. He may simply enter and leave through a roof vent or he may use a jumper wire to "fool" the electrical system.

• *Electronic eye alarms:* These rate no better than door and window alarms. They operate like automatic supermarket doors. When an invisible beam is broken, a silent alarm is tripped. Since the eye can be moved and aimed easily, it can be shifted to cover doors, windows, walls or a safe. Like door and window alarms, these systems are easy to breach using optical equipment to discover their position from a safe vantage point. Once the burglar spots them, he just works around them.

Effective Alarms

• *Proximity alarms:* Usually, they are activated by noise. Microphones are placed throughout an area and are activated when the premises are empty. They are sensitive to any noise they are programmed to register. They are generally very effective. *One weakness:* The last person to leave will activate the system. If anyone wishes to return, he must telephone the monitor, giving a code number and the length of time he expects to be in. If a burglar spots this kind of activity, he may (among other things) place a miniature recorder near the phone and learn the code. *Solution:* Code numbers, security information and schedules must be protected and changed frequently.

Tip: If you're shopping for an alarm, check out systems used by drugstores in your area. They are generally the best.

Key and Safe Advice

As vulnerable as they are, keys are the most cost-effective security device. *Ways to make those keys significantly more secure:*

• Stamp "Do Not Duplicate" on keys. It's not foolproof, but it helps to hinder unauthorized key copying.

• Use locks that require very hard-to-get key blanks. Some blanks are secure, that is, licensed keymakers don't stock the blanks; they must be acquired from the lockmaker. There is a delay—not long, but worthwhile.

• Many lock combinations (those which can be adjusted) are set to the user's birthday, Social Security number, phone number, or some other obvious set of digits. And crooks know that. In "casing" a potential burglary site, sophisticated thieves gather all the obvious numbers, and usually open the safe quite easily.

If none of the numbers work, the burglar looks in the "obvious" places for hiding the number: In the executive's diary or calendar, under the desk pad.

Recommendation: Don't use a related number. Memorize the digits and don't put them in "safe" places.

• *Signatures.* For important papers, sign your name in ink and with an *italic* pen. It's very hard to forge.

How to Spot Fake ID

Best identification: Photograph, physical description and signature. Other safeguards:

Repeat some information from the ID card back to the holder, but make a small mistake in repetition. Example: Is your address 733 Lake Dr.? (743 is the real number). Imposters are often unfamiliar with details.

Don't accept IDs that have the name of the state or issuing agency typed in instead of printed. Also, a typographical error is almost always a sign of a fake.

Check wear patterns on old cards. A genuine card will be worn mostly around the edges from handling. Some forgers artificially age cards, which gives a uniform look of wear all over the card.

Look for raised edges around photographs, which is a sign that a substitution has been made.

Feel for flaws in laminated cards, another sign of tampering.

Compare the typewriter face on various parts of the card. Reject it if there is a mismatch.

Check the holder's signature against the one on the ID.

Beware: Birth certificates are poor IDs because they fail to describe the adult using them. Better: A driver's license, passport or credit card (that can be checked to see if stolen).

Source: *The National Notary Magazine.*

Before You Buy a Safe

Most home safes on the market today are designed to protect against either fire or theft, but not both. So, unless you are willing to break your bank account for a dual-purpose supersafe, the best solution is to buy one of each type. Manufacturers suggest welding the theft safe inside the fire safe, and then bolting the whole thing to a concrete wall or floor.

What to look for:

Burglar-resistant safes. You generally get what you pay for. Minimum advisable specifications: A half-inch-thick solid steel door and quarter-inch-thick solid steel walls. (Aim: To prevent a thief from peeling away the walls with a crowbar.) Also: Make sure the safe has a relocking device in addition to a good-quality lock. If the lock is tampered with, the device automatically relocks the bolts.

Fire-resistant safes. Recommended for most homes: A safe that can withstand a temperature of 1,850°F for two hours.

Prices depend on the size of the safe, the specifications of the materials or the rating of the model. And, for burglar-resistant safes, the complexity of locks and relocking devices adds to the cost.

Money saver: A used safe. The cost is 20% to 40% lower than comparable new ones.

Retirement Planning

Arithmetic to Do Before You Retire

How to size up your financial situation:

1. List your assets. Include income-producing assets (stocks, bonds, other annuity-generating insurance policies, real estate, company profit-sharing plans), plus non-income-producing assets (paid-up life insurance, furniture and household goods) and assets that require expenditures for maintenance (houses, cars, etc.). Estimate total dollar value, factoring in appreciation.
2. Figure out postretirement income. Add up income from assets, pensions and Social Security.
3. Calculate postretirement expenses, then deduct costs stemming from work (commuting, clothes). Next add on the cost of benefits (health insurance) that will no longer be covered by an employer. Estimate an annual dollar figure. Factor in inflation rate.
4. If postretirement expenses outstrip postretirement income, develop a plan for liquidating assets. Rule of thumb: The percentage of total capital that a retired person may spend annually begins at 5% at age 65, and increases by 1% every five years, until reaching 10% at age 80.

Bottom line: Only those whose postretirement expenses still outstrip total income at this point will have to cut back. Generally, a retired person needs 75% of his preretirement, after-tax income to maintain his present standard of living.

Pension Bigger Than Salary

A provision in ERISA (the 1974 pension law) makes it possible for a small, closely held corporation to provide its older insiders, in a relatively short time, with pension benefits substantially larger than their compensation—and with the cost fully deductible by the corporation.

Example: A Mr. Smith, having elected early retirement from a major corporation, starts up his own consulting corporation. He brings his wife into the business as an assistant and has two part-time employees to help her with various chores. He puts his wife on the books for $6,000 a year, although she's worth more. Even though he considers increasing her pay, he has prudent misgivings, because her earnings will only add to the taxable income on their joint return.

Taking advantage of ERISA, Smith sets up a defined-benefit pension plan (where benefit payout is fixed) for his corporation. Under the so-called *de minimis* provisions of ERISA, he can set his wife's defined benefit upon retirement at $10,000 a year—$4,000 more than her annual salary. She's able to escape the benefit limit of 100% of her annual salary because her salary is under $10,000.

To establish the $10,000 benefit, he must show actuarily what it would cost to provide her with a straight-life annuity of $10,000 a year at age 65. That's easy. All he has to do is ask a life insurance company how much such a policy could cost. *Answer:* $140,000 lump sum. Thus, if you figure an 8% annual interest, compounded, it works out that he must put away $10,000 a year for the 10 years—or a total of $100,000. Additionally, Mrs. Smith has to participate in the plan for ten years. Otherwise the $10,000 will be reduced.

What we've done is provide her a benefit worth $140,000, with $100,000 in tax-deductible dollars.

Another plus: If those dollars had been paid to Mrs. Smith as straight compensation (and assuming that Mr. and Mrs. Smith filed joint returns), she would have paid out a large sum in taxes over the next 10 years of employment by the corporation.

How Safe Is Your Pension?

How to check on the safety of your retirement income:

For employees of public companies: Basic information is included in the firm's annual report. Usually the size of a firm's unfunded pension liability and the size of its past service liability are disclosed in footnotes. More detailed information is available in the financial section of the firm's 10K report, filed with the Securities and Exchange Commission.

For employees of private companies: Everyone who is in a qualified plan (one approved by the IRS under the Code) has the right to obtain information about his pension from the trustees of the plan. They may be either internal or external trustees. The average person may not be able to decipher the information. If you can't, then take it to a pension expert, actuary, lawyer or accountant for an analysis. *Cost:* $500–$800. Whether you are examining pension information of public or private firms, you are seeking the same sort of basic information.

Principle: The size of a company's liability for retirement payouts is not as important as the assumptions about funding these liabilities. Like a mortgage, these obligations don't exist 100% in the present. Concern yourself with *how* the company expects to fund its liabilities.

Types of Liabilities

• *Unfunded pension liabilities.* The amount a firm expects to need over the next 20–30 years to supply vested workers with promised pension benefits. These figures are derived from various actuarial assumptions.

• *Past service liabilities.* Created when a company raises its pension compensation. For instance, a company may have been planning to provide 40% of compensation as a pension. One year, they may raise that to 45% and treat it retroactively.

Trouble Signs

• *A poor record on investing.* Compare the market value of the assets in the pension with their book value. If book value is more than market value, the trustees have not been investing wisely. *Point:* If the fund had to sell those assets today, there would be a loss. You might also get a bit nervous if the fund is still holding some obscure bonds or other fixed-income obligations issued at low rates years ago.

• *Funding assumptions are overstated.* Actuaries have a myriad of estimates on how long it takes to fund pension plans and what rate of return a company will get. *What to look at:*

Time frame: This should not be long. If the firm is funding over 40 years, you will want to know why and how, since 10–20 years is more customary. *Reason:* We don't have a crystal ball, and the investment world will be different in as little as 10 years from now. Assumptions made on 40 years may not hold up at all.

Rate of return: If a company assumes a conservative 6%–7% or less right now, you can be comfortable. If the assumed rate is 10% or more, you will want to know how they are going to meet that expectation for the entire fund over the long run.

Salary and wage scales: The company should be assuming an increase in compensation over years. Most plans have such provisions. They must start funding now for future salary increases.

Assumptions about the employee turnover rate: These should be consistent with the historically documented turnover of the company. If a firm has a very low turnover rate and assumes a 4% turnover, the company will be underfunded at some time. Estimates should be conservative.

To assess your own status in a corporate pension plan, see *how many years you have been vested.*

Many people have the illusion that they are fully vested for maximum pensions after only five years or so. In truth, companies couldn't afford to fully vest people with such short service. They may offer some token pension for such service. But most people are not fully vested until they have worked for the firm for 10 or even 20 years, and then they might be vested only to the extent of their accrued pension to date, not the full pension expected at normal retirement. With so much job-hopping in the past two decades, an individual's pension-fund status may be much less than imagined.

Employees of troubled or even bankrupt companies need not panic. Trustees of the plan have an obligation to the vested employees. The assets of the plan are segregated, and no creditor can reach them. In fact, as a creditor, the corporate pension plan can grab some corporate assets under certain circumstances. And if there has been gross mismanagement of pension funds, stockholders of a closely held company can be held personally liable.

Source: James E. Conway, president of the Ayco Corporation, a consulting firm specializing in executive finances. Ayco is located at 1 Wall St., Albany, NY 12205.

Borrow from Your Own Retirement Plan and Pay Yourself Deductible Interest

Pay interest to yourself, deduct the interest you pay, then *receive the same interest tax free*, when you repay the loan. Sounds weird—but this tax-saving strategy makes sense—dollars and cents.

How: Borrow from your own qualified retirement plan. The IRS says that this is possible even when the plan covers only a *single* company employee. However, key employees aren't allowed to deduct the interest on these loans.

Requirements:

• The loan money must be used for a purpose (e.g., investment) for which interest is deductible (not personal or consumer purposes).

• The plan must specifically allow borrowing to all covered employees on a nondiscriminatory basis.

• The loan must bear a reasonable rate of interest, be adequately secured, and be repaid within five years. *Exception to five year rule:* An extended repayment period is permitted for loans for the purchase or improvement of your principal residence.

- The amount of the loan cannot be larger than (1) $50,000 less your highest outstanding loan balance in the prior 12 months, or (2) half of your vested plan benefits ($10,000 if your vested benefits are under $20,000), whichever is less.

The vested portion of your retirement plan benefits, which you are borrowing against, *can* be used as security for the loan.

Source: Irving Blackman, partner of Blackman, Kallick & Co., 180 N. LaSalle St., Chicago 60601.

An IRA Loophole That Sounds Almost Too Good to Be Legal

Contributions to an IRA must be in *cash only* (or gold or silver coins of the US or any state-issued coins acquired by an IRA after October 22, 1988), not stocks, bonds or other property. And, if you sell anything to raise your contribution, you must pay tax on any capital gain. *Tip:* Sell stocks that have *declined* in value. You can fund the IRA and also get a capital loss on the sale. Furthermore, if you desire, your IRA can repurchase the stocks immediately. The wash sale rules shouldn't apply, as you and your IRA are separate legal entities.

Withdraw Savings From IRA Before 59½, Pay the Penalty, and You're Still Way Ahead

A *deductible* IRA can be a better place to keep your savings than a money fund or regular savings account, even if you plan to use the money before you retire. That's because the tax advantages of a deductible IRA contribution are so great that they can outweigh the penalty that applies when funds are withdrawn from the IRA before age 59½.

Key: IRA contributions are made with pretax dollars. A person in the 28% bracket who earns an extra $1,000 has only $720 to invest after paying taxes. But the *entire* $1,000 can be put in an IRA and be ready to earn even more tax-free interest.

Thus, for an individual in the 28% tax bracket, an investment in a deductible IRA earning 8% interest would be superior to a taxable investment earning the same 8%, in spite of the IRA's early withdrawal penalty, if the money is left in the IRA for eight years. (If you are in a higher tax bracket for any reason or the IRA earns more than 8%, the breakeven point would be less than eight years.)

Source: Jill A. Harris, CFA, Arthur Young & Co., 277 Park Ave., New York 10172.

Cars

Making the Best Deal on a New Car

Determine a fair price by figuring what that car costs the dealer. This can be done by subtracting the markup on the base sticker price (before options are added on) and then subtracting the markup on the options.

The markup on base sticker prices generally is as follows:

10% on economy cars (Chevette, Omni, Fiesta).

12% on subcompacts (Pinto, Monza).

15% on compacts (Nova, Volare, Fairmont).

16% on sporty cars (Camaro, Firebird).

18% on intermediates (Malibu, Cutlass, Granada).

20% on smaller luxury cars (Monte Carlo, Grand Prix, Thunderbird).

22% on full-size cars (Caprice, Galaxie).

25% on luxury cars (Cadillac, Lincoln).

25% on pickups and vans.

The markup option is as follows:

30% on appearance and convenience items (vinyl roof, air conditioning, power windows, radio).

20% on performance items (radials, five-speed transmission, heavy-duty suspension or cooling system).

After subtracting the markups to determine dealer cost, add $125 for dealer overhead. Add on freight charges (itemized on the sticker) and also $100 profit for the dealer (he'll still get an additional 2% rebate from the manufacturer). The final figure is what you should pay for the car you want. Shop around until you find a dealer who'll sell it for that price (give or take $100). Don't be pressured to take a car that is loaded with unnecessary options from the dealer's inventory.

Car Owner's Guide to Saving Money

• Buy bargain tires marked "blems." They are perfectly serviceable except for minor cosmetic blemishes on sidewalls.

• Lengthen the life of old windshield-wiper blades by rubbing the edges with a knife or the striking part of a matchbook cover. This exposes the softer material underneath and improves the wiping ability of the blades.

• Preserve the car's finish by washing it with cold or lukewarm water. But never wash the finish with hot water.

• Run the air-conditioner at least 10 minutes every week. This procedure will maintain coolant pressure and avoid costly air-conditioner breakdowns.

• When you stop for service, get out of the car and watch gas-station attendants carefully, particularly if you have an out-of-state license. When the oil is checked, make sure the dipstick is inserted all the way. Some attendants may show you a dipstick that indicates oil is low, then use an empty can and pretend to add a quart of oil.

• Clean corrosion off the battery terminals. Use a wire brush or steel wool to scrape battery posts and cable clamps. Clean the top surface with a mild solution of baking soda and water. Don't let it seep under cell caps.

• Prevent wind resistance, which cuts performance up to five miles per gallon, by keeping the car windows closed while driving.

• Be aware that every fives miles per hour over 50 cuts fuel performance by two miles per gallon.

Choosing a Mechanic

You'll likely avoid that incompetent or dishonest auto mechanic by sticking to repair shops approved by the Automobile Association of America. If the garage carries AAA's tricolor sign (the inspection program now includes more than 2,000 shops in 24 states), you can be confident that repair bays, tools and mechanics are up to snuff. *Another good sign:* A mechanic certified by the National Institute of Auto Service Excellence, particularly in the system you need repaired.

Source: *Money,* Rockefeller Center, New York 10020, monthly.

Your Car Won't Start

Before the mechanic replaces your alternator, make sure he checks its belt. It could mean the difference between a $200 job and a $20 part.

Right and Wrong Jumper Cables

Car jumper cables that work from cigarette lighter to cigarette lighter aren't very effective. The wires can't carry enough amps to do an efficient job, particularly in cold weather, when it takes more power to get a car started. Under optimal conditions—with the battery just below charge and the outside temperature moderate—it can take 10–15 minutes to get your battery working. *Better:* Old-fashioned jumper cables that connect battery to battery. Used properly, they're safer, more efficient and much faster.

Source: Tony Assenza, racing car buff and editor of *Motor Trend*, 8490 Sunset Blvd., Los Angeles 90067, monthly.

Rustproofing Scams

Dealer-applied rustproofing should be done as soon as you buy the car. But *be careful.* Read the fine print. Most "guarantees" give you only the cost of rustproofing in case of rust. Make sure the guarantee states that the dealer will repair or replace rusted body panels.

Some rustproofers demand that you return every year at a *strictly specified time* in order to keep the guarantee in effect. They'll usually hit you with a $25 refresher-application bill. Find a rustproofer who will give you at least a month's leeway on that return date.

Rip-off artists simply drill the holes and put in a plastic plug, never applying the rustproofing agent at all. When you get the car home, take off the plugs and insert a screwdriver in the holes. The agent, still a little runny, will come off on the screwdriver. If it's not there, get your money back.

You can save money with a do-it-yourself rustproofing kit. You'll probably do a more conscientious job than a mechanic anyway, and the materials are equal in quality.

What Car Rental Agencies Don't Tell You

- *Automatic drop-off can be a rip-off on late-night rented-car returns.* Unlike normal rental-car check-in, where the clerk totals up the costs and gives you a copy of the bill, automatic drop-offs require you to return all copies. You often don't get a copy until your credit-card company has billed you. *Protection alternatives:* Return your rental car during business hours. Make a copy of the rental form before returning it, noting your entry of the final mileage. Don't pay your credit-card bill *until* you get the car-rental bill and make sure their figures agree with yours. If they have overcharged you, dispute the bill and let the credit-card company know about the problem.
- *If you damage a rented car, it can cost you more than you expect.* The first $250 or even $500 is now on you. Deductible used to be $100, but most chains quietly raised it recently. And you can't take a tax deduction for a $500 casualty loss, because it's not your car. *Best bet:* Avoid the increased risk by paying a $2–$3-a-day fee. Or get your car from a dealer who rents as a sideline. His rates are lower. The deductible is usually still $100.
- *Pay traffic tickets you get when driving a rented car.* Many rental companies give the police your name, address and your *home state* license number if you get a ticket. You risk being picked up as a scofflaw back home.
- *Don't pay for more insurance than you need on a rented car.* Rental agents routinely encourage customers to pay around $5 a day for optional collision coverage. Chances are, however, that your own personal-car policy may extend coverage to a rented car. Check the insurance policy before signing up for unnecessary coverage.
- *Be wary if the car rental agency asks for the name of your auto insurance company.* Chances are they're giving you only *secondary* liability insurance coverage. That means *their* insurance company won't pay until your own insurance is exhausted (and your own premiums will go up).
- *Give a rental car the onceover before driving away in it.* Check the headlights, turn signals and brakes. Squirt the windshield washer to be sure that there is fluid. Check the oil level. Drive it around the block before taking it on the expressway.

Real Estate

When Buying a New Condominium

Before signing any contract for a new condominium, which is harder to check out than an established condominium, buyers should study the prospectus for any of these pitfalls:

The prospectus includes a plan of the unit you are buying, showing rooms of specific dimensions. But the plan omits closet space. Result: The living space you are buying is probably smaller than you think.

The prospectus includes this clause: The interior design shall be substantially similar. Result: The developer can alter both the size and design of your unit.

The common charges set forth in the prospectus are unrealistically low. Buyers should never rely on a developer's estimate of common charges. Instead: They should find out the charges at similarly functioning condominiums.

Common charges include: Electricity for hallways and outside areas, water, cleaning, garbage disposal, insurance for common areas, pool maintenance, groundskeeping, legal and accounting fees, reserves for future repairs.

Variation on the common-charge trap: The developer is paying common charges on unsold units. But these charges are unrealistically low. Reason: The developer has either underinsured, underestimated the taxes due, omitted security expenses or failed to set up a reserve fund.

The prospectus includes this clause: The seller will not be obligated to pay monthly charges for unsold units. Result: The owners of a partially occupied condominium have to pay for all operating expenses.

The prospectus warns about the seller's limited liability. But an unsuspecting buyer may still purchase a condominium unit on which back monthly charges are due, or even on which there's a lien for failure to pay back carrying charges.

The prospectus makes no mention of parking spaces. Result: You must lease from the developer.

The prospectus is imprecise about the total number of units to be built. Result: Facilities are inadequate for the number of residents.

The prospectus includes this clause: Transfer of ownership (of the common property from the developer to the homeowners' association) will take place 60 days after the last unit is sold. Trap: The developer deliberately does not sell one unit, keeps on managing the condominium and awards sweetheart maintenance and operating contracts to his subcontractors.

The prospectus specifies that the developer will become the property manager of the functioning condominium. But the language spelling out monthly common charges and management fees is imprecise. Result: The owners cannot control monthly charges and fees.

Source: Dorothy Tymon, author, *The Condominium: A Guide for the Alert Buyer,* Golden-Lee Books, Brooklyn, NY.

Traps in Homeowner's Insurance

Many home buyers hastily purchase homeowner's insurance to qualify for their mortgage. Problem: They don't understand the choices involved in insuring a home.

Basic insurance: If a fire or other catastrophe destroys your home, you get the replacement cost, which is enough to rebuild the home to its original state. You carry at least 80% of the replacement cost. What you don't get: The market value of the home so that you can go out and buy a similar one. Land value and neighborhood are inherent in market value, yet unrelated to replacement cost.

Carry at least 80% of the home's replacement value. If you don't, the insurance company penalizes you by the percentage you underinsure.

Example: You have a $100,000 house, and carry only $60,000 on it. That is three-quarters of the $80,000 required. If you have $20,000 worth of damage from a fire, you will get only $15,000, or three-quarters of your damage. If you were insured for $80,000, you would get full coverage.

How to ascertain replacement cost:

Most insurance companies will inspect your house if it is worth over $100,000.

Your broker has a replacement-cost guide. This determines the cost of the average home by computing the number of rooms and square feet. It is an educated guess.

If your home was custom built, get an independent appraisal.

Replacement cost versus actual cash value: Replacement cost is only useful when you rebuild your house. If you decide to walk away and buy another house, you will only get actual cash value. What it is: Replacement value minus depreciation.

Example: You have a 50-year-old home worth $100,000 and $80,000 worth of insurance. You might get only $40,000 if you decide not to build, because depreciation could take away as much as 50% of the payment. (Depreciation computed by an insurance company is not related to depreciation for tax purposes. Depreciation is rarely in excess of 50% on a home.)

Inflation protection: Most insurance companies automatically increase coverage by whatever it costs to rebuild a home in your area. This automatic increase has been running about 10%.

Check out: Whether inflation increases are granted annually, semiannually, or quarterly. *Problem:* If inflation is running 10% and you have a disaster after six months, you may have insufficient coverage. *Best:* Ask for an endorsement that increases protection quarterly. It costs little. Some insurers don't charge for it.

Other coverage included in a homeowner's policy:

The cost of staying in a hotel or renting a temporary apartment or house while your own home is repaired. Coverage: Up to 20% of insurance of the home's contents (furniture, china, clothing, etc.). Coverage: 50% of the insured value of the house.

Third-party liability: Protection in case anyone is injured on your property. Example: A party guest slips on a rug and breaks an ankle bone. Or: Someone is injured through some action of yours off your property. Example: You hit someone with a golf ball.

Appurtenant structures: A garage or shed. Coverage: 10% of home coverage.

Theft away from home: This covers a suitcase stolen from your locked car, etc. Caution: This coverage is limited and optional in some states.

Examine policies for restricted coverage on jewelry, furs, silverware, fine art, money and securities. Schedule high-value items so that you and the insurer agree on value before there is a loss.

Keep accurate records of your possessions. Don't keep the records where they can be destroyed with the rest of your home.

Seek the broadest coverage possible within your budget. Some homeowner's policies are little more than fire-insurance contracts. Caution: No homeowner's policy covers floods. Flood coverage must be obtained separately. The best policies, known as all-risk policies, cover nearly everything and take the burden of proof of coverage away from you. They make the insurance company prove it is excluded from the contract.

Example: A deer jumped through a picture window. The deer panicked and tore through the house. The entire interior was destroyed, since the deer either broke or bled on nearly everything. A standard policy would not cover this incident. Under an all-risk policy, the company must pay unless it can prove the incident falls within a specific exclusion from coverage set out in the policy.

Look for credits for higher deductibles, particularly percentage deductibles.

Example: You insure your house for $100,000. Instead of getting a $500 deductible, you can get a credit for a ½% deductible. However, realize that when the amount of the insurance is raised 10% the next year, your deductible will rise proportionately, from $500 to $550.

Look for credits for burglary and fire alarms.

Look into companies that pay dividends.

Source: Judith L. Robinson, CPCU, vice-president of general insurance brokers H&R Philips, 622 Third Ave., New York 10017.

Figures to Check at Real Estate Closing

Monthly payments.

Per diem figures for utilities, taxes and/or interest.

The broker's commission.

The rent, security deposits and/or interest on deposits that have not as yet been transferred.

A charge for utility bills already paid.

A charge for loan fees already paid.

A contractor, attorney, appraiser or some other party to the contract who has not been paid.

How to Minimize Flood Damage

Flooded basements can be "good." If flood reaches your property, water inside will equalize underground pressure outside and prevent collapse of basement walls. Don't pump out basement until flood recedes.

If you have no second floor: Remember, water inside a building often gets no higher than two or three feet. Use high shelves for valuables (including furnace motor).

Keep underground fuel tank full. Otherwise, it can buoy up to the surface, causing foundation walls to collapse. (If no fuel is available, fill tank with water.)

Reducing Real Estate Tax by Challenging Assessments

Effective real estate tax is tax rate multiplied by *assessed value.* There is not much an individual can do about tax rate, but assessment can often be challenged successfully. *Requirements:* Owner must show either that property is overvalued or that assessment is higher than on comparable property in same area.

When to ask for reduction:

- Just before making necessary repairs of damages or deterioration that has lowered the value of property.
- Local tax records err in description by overstating size or income.
- Net income drops due to factors beyond owner's control.
- When price paid for building in arm's-length

transaction is lower than the assessed value.

What to do:

• Determine the *ratio* of the assessed value to the present market value. Compare against average ratios of similar properties recently sold in same area. *Sources:* Ratios available to public in tax districts. Real estate brokers, professional assessors can also be consulted.

• Check tax records for description of property, income.

• Consult lawyer on strength of case, whether it can be handled by informal talk with assessor, how much it will cost if formal proceeding or appeal are neccessary.

Screening Potential Real Estate Investments

Rules of thumb can be dangerous if relied on exclusively for real estate investments, but they do offer a quick and simple way to screen properties. *Two rules:* (1) Don't pay more than 6–7 times the gross annual rent, or 10 times the net operating income, unless the going rate in the area is consistently higher. (2) Think twice if operating expenses eat up from 50% to 70% of gross rentals in an apartment building (leaving 30–50% gross income), depending on geographic area. Major costs include vacancy and collection losses, repairs and maintenance, management fees, heating oil or gas, before deducting taxes and mortgage payments.

Caution: In-depth analysis of area and property, plus expert legal and real estate advice is still a must before final decision is made.

How Real Estate Investors Get Tricked

The urge to invest in real estate, which is still strong in most parts of the country, exposes buyers to sharp practices by sellers.

The most common distortion is a claim of high-paying tenants. If the rent roll of a commercial building shows that nine tenants pay $6–$8 per square foot and three pay $12, find out who the high-paying tenants are. One may be the building owner, and the others may be affiliated with the seller.

Any fudging of current and future income can cost an investor tens of thousands of dollars. In a small building, where the seller reports that 10 tenants pay $400 a month ($48,000 a year), if buildings in the area sell for six times gross, the market price would be $288,000. But suppose the owner had prepared to sell the building by raising the rents from $350 to $400 a month. That increase in the rent roll cost the buyer $36,000 (the difference beween six times $48,000 in annual rents and six times $42,000).

Even worse would be the impact on future rent increases. If the rents in the building were close to market before the increase, the owner may well have offered tenants a free month's rent or a delayed increase. A delayed increase means that the buyer will not realize as much income as forecast. A free month's rent means that the actual increase in rents was only $17 an apartment, not $50. If the new owner tries to jump rents well above that, tenants may move.

Other seller claims that buyers must investigate:

• Low operating expenses. Sellers may be operating the building themselves to avoid a management fee. If buyers cannot take care of the building personally, this fee must be added to real operating expenses. And if sellers do not factor it in, the bank will, when it calculates the maximum supportable mortgage.

• Reasonable property tax. If the building has not been assessed for several years, the buyer may have a substantial tax bite on the next reassessment. Also, the seller may have made an addition to the building that has not yet been recorded with the tax assessor. As a precaution, ask the local assessment office for a tax card or listing sheet. It will show the building's assessment and when it was assessed. If it was assessed a year and a half ago and there has been no significant addition to the building, reassessment may not hurt the buyer. But if it has not been assessed for eight years, there could be a significant tax boost.

While checking the tax card or listing sheet, check the owner's property description against the one listed. If the owner says that 20,000 square feet are being sold but the tax card says 15,000 square feet, there has been some addition to the structure that has not been recorded, and therefore, has not been assessed. Or, there may be an assessment error that, when corrected, will raise costs.

• Low insurance premiums. Is coverage in line with the structure's current value? What does the policy cover? Ask to see the policy. Ask an insurance adviser if coverage is insufficient, how much more will proper coverage cost?

• Energy efficient. Verify the owner's claim with the local utility to determine actual energy costs. Also check with regulatory commissions to see whether utility companies are scheduled to increase their tariffs.

• A real buy. Check the income statement with those of comparable buildings in the area. Consult the annual income and expense analysis by geographical area and building type with the Institute of Real Estate Management (430 N. Michigan Ave., Chicago 60611).

Source: Thomas L. O'Dea, O'Dea & Co., Inc., 2150 Country Club Rd., Winston-Salem, NC 27103.

Tips for Sellers on Selecting a Real Estate Agent

• Avoid the trap of listing property with relative or friend in the real estate business. Seek out an experienced, full-time agent, preferably one who *specializes* in your type of property or neighborhood.

• Watch out for *supersalespeople.* They often push *easy* properties. If you feel uncomfortable with the agent, or there's some hangup about the property, *find someone else.*

• Real estate office is important, too. It should be attractive, easily accessible, and open seven days a week for residential business. Agency should be a member of a multiple listing service and well regarded by financing sources. *Note:* Try to speak with the head of the firm. If you call in cold, you will get (and be stuck with) the broker who is on duty that day.

Ways of Listing Property for Sale

• *Open listing:* The owner reserves the right to sell the property himself or to retain brokers.

• *Exclusive agency:* No other broker will be hired as long as the original broker is retained (usually for a specified period), but this doesn't prevent the owner from selling the property himself.

• *Exclusive right to sell:* The broker gets his commission when the property is sold whether by the broker, the owner, or anyone else.

• *Multiple listing:* Brokers combine to sell properties listed with any member of the brokers' pool. The brokers themselves split commissions between the listing and selling broker.

If no time is specified, the listing is good for a "reasonable" time. The owner can revoke the listing at any time before the broker has earned his commission, provided he acts in good faith and doesn't revoke when negotiations have been substantially completed.

If a time is specified, the agreement will end as stipulated. It would continue only if the owner has waived the time limit by accepting the services of the broker, or if the owner has acted in bad faith (as by postponing agreement with a buyer until after the time limit). In some states, if the listing is for a specified time, the owner can revoke only up until the time the broker has put money and effort into the listing contract.

If nothing is said, the broker will earn his commission on finding a buyer ready, willing and able to buy on the terms specified. The owner, to protect himself, should ask for a provision under which payment of the commission will depend on closing the deal and full payment.

Estate Planning

How Much Life Insurance You Need

First step: Determine what the surviving members' short- and long-term economic needs are likely to be. Then, estimate the amount of these needs covered by available resources (savings, home equity, existing insurance, pension benefits, veterans' benefits and Social Security). Buy only enough life insurance to make up the deficit between needs and available resources.

How to determine needs:

Immediate cash for death-related expenses. For uninsured medical costs, funeral expenses, debts, taxes and estate-settlement fees (including the lawyer's bill). Minimum amount of cash: $4,000.

Readjustment fund. Takes economic pressure off the family, allowing them to make important decisions without haste. Optimum size: Six to 12 months of the lost net income of a working parent, or the one-year cost of replacing the family services of a nonworking parent.

Mortgage funds. Mortgage-canceling life insurance gives survivors relatively low-cost housing (that is, they pay only taxes and upkeep). If they decide to sell the house, insurance relieves the pressure to sell too quickly at a distress price.

Family income. Make two budgets and periodically review them. One budget applies if the father's income is lost. The other applies either to replace a working mother's lost income or the cost of replacing her services at home.

Emergency fund. For an unexpected crisis, such as a major illness. Amount: About $2,000 (adjust for the size and health of the family).

Widow's income. Drops in proportion to her decreasing financial responsibility to the children. After the children are on their own, she may not need extra income if she remarries or takes a job. Otherwise, she would need extra income if she does not remarry or work, for Social Security benefits stop when her youngest child turns 18 and will not resume until she reaches 60.

Special funds. To cover the cost of the children's college educations, and so on.

Some guidelines:

Comparison shop for price and quality of insurance coverage.

Fill short-term needs, such as mortgage protection or supplemental income during the children's early years, with the lowest-cost term insurance available. Fill long-term needs with the least expensive whole-life insurance.

Know your life insurance needs before talking to insurance agents. Don't get pressured into the wrong purchase.

Useful rule of thumb:

After the death of its principal income-producer, a family requires 75% of its former after-tax income to maintain its standard of living, according to a Citibank report. It must, according to that report, have at least 60% to get along at all.

Here is the amount of life insurance (in terms of annual earnings multiples) needed to provide this income at different ages (taking into account Social Security benefits and assuming the insurance proceeds were invested to produce an after-inflation return of 5% a year, with the entire principal consumed over survivor's life expectancy).

Present	**Your Present Earnings**				
Age	**$15M**	**$23.5M**	**$30M**	**$40M**	**$65M**
25 years					
75%	4.5	6.5	7.5	7.5	7.5
60%	3.0	4.5	5.0	5.0	5.5
35 years					
75%	6.5	8.0	8.0	8.0	7.5
60%	4.5	5.5	6.0	6.0	6.0
45 years					
75%	8.0	8.5	8.5	8.0	7.5
60%	6.0	6.5	6.5	6.0	6.0
55 years					
75%	7.0	7.5	7.0	7.0	6.5
60%	5.5	5.5	5.5	5.5	5.0

While the chart shows insurance needs, it would be more useful to say that it shows capital requirements. Those requirements can be met by life insurance or through savings and investments, employee benefits or inheritance. Thus, to the extent that the independent capital resources are built up, insurance needs diminish.

Example: An individual, aged 55, with earnings of $40,000 and a net worth of $240,000, instead of requiring insurance in the face amount of $280,000, could get by with $40,000 in life insurance coverage and still meet the seven-time-earnings multiple indicated by the chart.

Understanding Term Insurance

Term insurance is usually the least expensive form of insurance to get for a maximum of five years.

The choices:

Yearly renewable term. The rates start low and rise annually as your age (which increases the risk) goes up. Choose this policy if you're in a short-term venture (a construction project or a short-term contract).

Five- and ten-year term insurance. Appropriate for a person starting a high-risk or highly leveraged business when the bank may insist that the entrepreneur's life be covered by a large policy for a specified period of time. The premium is averaged out on an annual basis over the life of the policy.

Yearly renewable term policy with a reversion to lower premiums on evidence of insurability. This is a recent development. At a specified time (usually after four or five years), if you pass a medical exam, the premiums can be reduced by perhaps 35% of what they might have been. *Example:* If your insurance premium starts at $1,000 a year and climbs $200 annually, you must pass an exam during the fifth year to get the premium lowered to $1,200. Potential problem: Bad health at the time of the examination will negate the possibility of lowering the premium.

Avoid term insurance even for the short haul if you are almost 70 years old. Since the risk at that age is so high, the point at which term and straight-premium rate would cross would be attained within five years. At that point, a permanent (or straight) life policy is best.

If you need life insurance for more than five years, permanent insurance is usually best.

Reason: The total acquisition price usually evens out over a period of 10 years. If the buyer is relatively young, say in his thirties, the cash value of the policy may increase at a greater rate than the premium after the third year. The straight-life policy holder may borrow on the cash value at a tax-deductible, low rate of interest.

Alternative: Some creative insurance agents combine the two types of insurance coverage, thus lowering premium costs and ensuring cash value at a specific time.

Source: Leon Sicular, president, Leon H. Sicular Associates, 350 Fifth Ave., New York 10001.

Tough-Minded Estate Planning

It may seem callous to even think about taxes when a loved one faces a life-threatening illness. But if tax planning is ignored at that point, assets carefully accumulated over a lifetime may be squandered unnecessarily. For many facing a final illness, dealing with these matters provides a life-oriented focus that helps them to combat depression and achieve a sense of completion in seeing that their affairs are well ordered. *Some things to consider:*

- *Gifts by the patient.* In many cases, estate taxes can be saved by making gifts to family members and other intended beneficiaries. An unlimited amount may be transferred tax free provided no one person receives more than $10,000. The maximum tax-free gift per recipient can increase to $20,000 if the patient's spouse is still alive and consents to treat each gift as having been jointly made.

Under the old law, gifts made within three years of death were figured back into the taxable estate. The 1981 tax act repealed this "contemplation-of-death" rule in most cases. *One major exception:* The old rule still applies to gifts of life insurance.

- *Gifts to the patient.* This tactic may be useful when the patient doesn't have enough property to take full advantage of the estate tax exemption ($600,000). *Reason:* Property that passes through the decedent's estate gets what's known as a stepped-up basis. That is, the person who inherits it is treated for income tax purposes as though he bought it and paid what it is worth on the date of death. (Or what it was worth six months after the date of death if the executor chooses this alternative date to set the value of the taxable estate.)

Example: Mr. Jones, a cancer patient, has $150,000 worth of assets. His wife has a large estate, including $75,000 worth of stock that has a tax basis of $10,000. That means there's $65,000 worth of taxable gain built into the stock. She gives the stock to her husband. (There's no tax on gifts between spouses.) Mr. Jones leaves the stock to the children. The children inherit the stock with the basis stepped up to $75,000. So if they turn right around and sell it for $75,000, there's no taxable gain. With these shares, Mr. Jones's estate is still under $600,000—the exempt amount. So the stepped-up basis is achieved without paying estate tax. And the property is taken out of Mrs. Jones's estate, where it might be taxed.

Caution: In most cases, it doesn't pay to use this tactic with property that will be bequeathed back to a spouse who gave it to the patient. Unless the gift was made more than a year before the date of death, stepped-up basis will be denied. But, when the patient is expected to survive for well over a year, this tactic can be quite useful.

Example: Mr. Smith owns a $150,000 rental property with a $25,000 tax basis. Mrs. Smith has a disease that will be fatal within two to five years. She has few assets of her own. So Mr. Smith gives her the building and inherits it back from her a few years later with the basis stepped up to $150,000. This substantially increases his depreciation deductions if he keeps the building and eliminates any taxable gain if he sells it.

- *Loss property:* In general there is a tax disadvantage in inheriting property that is worth less than its original cost. *Reason:* Its tax basis is stepped down to its date-of-death value and the potential loss deduction is forfeited. If the patient has substantial income, it might pay to sell the property and deduct the losses. But it doesn't pay to generate losses that are more than $3,000 in excess of the patient's capital gains. *Reason:* These excess losses can't be deducted currently, and there's likely to be no future year's income on which to deduct them. *Alternative:* Sell the loss property at its current value to a close family member. *Result:* The patient's loss on the sale is nondeductible, because the purchaser is a family member. But any future gains the family member realizes will be nontaxable to the extent of the previously disallowed loss.

• *Charitable gifts.* In some cases, bequests to charitable organizations should be made before death. *Benefit:* Current income tax deductions. But it's important not to give too much away. This tactic may generate more deductions than the patient can use.

• *Flower bonds.* Certain series of US Treasury bonds can be purchased on the open market for substantially less than their full face value, because they pay very low interest. But if a decedent owns these so-called flower bonds on the date of death, they can be credited against the estate tax at their full face value.

Timing: Flower bonds should be bought when death is clearly imminent. There's little point in holding them for substantial periods before death because they yield very little income. On the other hand, it does no good for the estate to purchase them after death because they won't be applied against the estate tax. In some cases, flower bonds have been bought on behalf of a patient in a coma by a relative or trustee who holds a power of attorney. The IRS has attacked these purchases. But the courts have, so far, sided with the taxpayer.

Naming the Right Executor

It's a touching gesture to name a spouse or grown child an executor. And they'll also get to keep the estate's administration fee (which can run to 4% or more of the gross estate). The fee would otherwise go to an outsider.

True, the relative (most often the widow) may not have any specialized knowledge of estate administration matters, but so what? An experienced lawyer and accountant can be hired to see things through. You might even supply a few recommended professionals to help when the time comes.

Life—and death—aren't that simple, however. *Point:* The executor is personally responsible for estate-tax liabilities and late filings, as well as for making sure that the estate is distributed in accord with the will. He or she is not relieved of this responsibility by delegating to a lawyer the task of "doing whatever is necessary."

Exception: In a very few cases, courts have waived personal penalties when an executor with no business or tax experience, and with scant formal education, had relied upon a seasoned lawyer to take care of the matter. *Warning:* The great weight of court authority is to the contrary.

An executor also may have to pick up the bill personally if he or she distributes estate assets to beneficiaries so that there isn't enough left to pay federal taxes. That would happen if there was any reason to suspect that the IRS would still be owed money.

Example: An IRS agent warns the executor that the value of shares in a closely held corporation as shown on the federal estate tax return probably will be jacked up.

The executor may also be held personally responsible for unpaid taxes if the IRS had not put him on notice that more taxes might be payable.

One case: An executor spoke to an officer of the bank where the decedent had conducted his business. She was informed that the decedent hadn't paid any federal tax on his considerable earnings for years. This should have alerted her to the fact that estate assets couldn't all be distributed to heirs without leaving enough for what Uncle Sam would demand. The IRS was paid out of her own funds.

Another liability: An heir can hold the executor personally responsible for the amount the heir may have lost through mismanagement of the estate's assets.

Other problems for a spouse: A spouse, in particular, may be too emotionally upset to do a competent job as executor. That has happened even when the spouse was an attorney with vast estate-tax experience. A spouse or other really close relative is also at a disadvantage in gathering all of the estate assets as required by law. Relatives and friends may insist that money or property which the decedent had lent to them really had been intended as gifts, with an alleged "understanding" that the advance would be forgotten when the decedent died. A widow would have the unpleasant task of trying to collect from her husband's relatives—or of having to sue them. A common occurrence in such cases: The widow instead fails to report assets of that type on the estate tax return, then gets caught by the IRS.

Another danger: An executor might regard her husband's will and its property dispositions as sacrosanct, to be honored at all costs—including the cost to herself.

Example: State laws generally allow a widow a certain percentage of her husband's estate, such as 35%, as dower rights. If he leaves her a lesser amount, she can "take against the will" and get this

35% at the expense of other beneficiaries. But, to preserve family sensitivities, the executor might refuse to tamper with her husband's instructions and hence would be shortchanging herself.

The saving on administrative fees is not large enough to make that the basis for selecting a family member. An individual is not subject to federal tax on what he or she inherits. But, if the widow is executor, the IRS may claim that part of what she inherited actually had been intended to be payment for administering the estate, and she will be assessed income tax on it.

The other side: Consider the potential expense and other consequences of being an executor. That should help to shape your response if a relative or friend flatters you by inviting you to serve as his executor. Even if they offer you a fee, it may not be worth it.

When Your Safe-Deposit Box Isn't Safe

It is unwise to keep anything in a safe-deposit box that may be needed quickly when the owner dies. At that time, a bank normally seals the box until legal proceedings (sometimes lengthy) take place.

Don't store:

Original will, cemetery deeds or burial instructions. (Keep them in a safe place at home or in a vault belonging to your lawyer, executor or accountant.)

Large amounts of *cash*. Money in a safe-deposit box is not working for you and suggests intent to evade income tax.

Unregistered property (such as jewelry or bearer bonds) belonging to *someone else*. Courts could presume these items to be your property, and proving otherwise might be difficult.

Store these:

Personal papers, such as birth and marriage certificates, military service or citizenship papers, important family records.

Jewelry, medals, rare coins, stamps, family heirlooms.

Original, signed, family or business documents, such as house deeds, mortgage papers, trust agreements, contracts, leases, court decrees.

Securities, registered or bearer.

Final check: Make sure someone knows where the safe-deposit box is and where the key is, too.

Important: Safe-deposit boxes taken out in corporate name *don't* get sealed upon the death of one of the principals. Might be *very* useful for closely held firms.

Use of Mutual Wills Can Forfeit Marital Deduction

A husband might want to leave a big chunk of property to his wife when he dies, but he may fear that she will make no provision to bequeath any of this property to *his* relatives or friends. She may feel the same way about leaving property to him. One solution to this dilemma is to have the spouses make *mutual wills*, in which each party agrees to leave inherited property to the survivor, who after death will leave specified property to designated relatives or friends of both parties.

Problem: The solution may create tax problems involving marital deductions on the estate tax return. If the wife, for example, was contractually bound by a mutual will to bequeath whatever remains of her late husband's property to, say, the children, his property *has not passed on to her without strings*. This deduction only applies if the property passes outright.

State law is important here to determine whether the property passing to her under her husband's will was really contractually subject to a condition. In one decision on this frequent issue, the court held that under *New York* law, a state resident is bound by such a restriction and hence the property earmarked for the children upon the death didn't qualify for the marital deduction because she didn't receive this property outright and without strings.

Indicated action: Check with tax counsel for the precedent in your state.

Source: David A. Siegel Estate, 67 T.C., No. 50.

Tax-Free Gifts to Family Save Estate Tax and Income Tax

Annual gifts up to $10,000 a year per recipient are not subject to gift tax. Married couples can give twice as much. Every year for the rest of your life, you and your spouse can jointly give $20,000 tax-free to each heir and reduce your taxable estate by the same amount.

Tax savings are impressive even if you're widowed or divorced. An individual with four married children and ten grandchildren can give the children, their spouses and their grandchildren $180,000 a year with no tax.

Avoiding tax on gifts over $10,000: Give a part interest each year. Or transfer property through an installment sale, taking back notes that are payable at annual intervals. *You can cancel these notes as they fall due.*

Gifts to reduce family's total income tax:

Transfer income-producing assets to low-bracket members. Children can earn up to $1,000 of income from the asset before the parent has to pay income tax in his/her higher tax bracket. (No gift tax if $10,000 limit is observed.)

When Not to Leave Everything to Spouse

If the estate will be *over* $600,000, it could be a mistake to leave everything to the widow, even if it reduces or eliminates the estate tax.

Reason: That's only the *first* estate tax. *The second estate tax* will come when the widow dies. If she did not remarry, there would be no marital deduction for her estate.

New York attorney Marvin W. Weinstein, who specializes in taxes and estate planning, suggests using *dual trusts* in some cases, with one qualified and the other not qualified for the marital deduction. Important when the objective is to provide liberally for the surviving spouse, but reduce estate taxes on transfers to the next generation.

A *marital trust* is eligible for the marital deduction from the estate tax, but it has the disadvantage that the assets will be taxed in the wife's estate when she dies.

By contrast, a *nonmarital trust* isn't eligible for the marital deduction from the estate tax. The assets are moved to the next generation without being taxed in the widow's estate when she dies. A typical non-marital trust would be one in which the widow gets all of the income as long as she lives, but on the death the principal passes to the children.

The two types of trust differ in the *degree of control* of the assets that the widow has. And there are legal/technical requirements that a good trust lawyer should handle.

These procedures are unnecessary if the estate is less than $600,000, because there's no estate tax below that.

Getting Your Money's Worth

Good Low-Priced Wines

Price isn't necessarily an indicator of quality in wine. Yes, superb wines are costly, but not all costly wines are superb.

Safest way to buy foreign wines: Rely on a good shipper. (The name appears on the neck or body label.) The shipper acts as the consumer's sampler and taster. By buying better vintages from a *selection of vineyards,* they maintain good consistency from year to year.

• Reliable shipper names to remember when buying French wines: *Louis Latour, Louis Jadot, Alexis Lichine,* and *Joseph Drohin.*

• For French and German wines: *Peter Sichel* and *Frank Schoonmaker.*

When buying reasonably priced *domestic* wines, there are two price levels to choose from:

• *Premium* California wines. Two reliable producers are *Beaulieu* and *Robert Mondavi.*

• *Standard* price range: *Charles Krug* and *Christian Brothers* are names to remember.

How about sherry? Many people are switching to it from martinis and other hard-liquor cocktails as an aperitif. Good Spanish sherries cost very little more than California brands. Two good buys: *Tio Pepe* and *Dry Fly.*

In general, heavily advertised foreign wines and sherries are overpriced. If you like *Mouton Cadet,* try a red Bordeaux from one of the French shippers. Substitute a German Liebfraumilch for *Blue Nun,* or a California rose for the popular *Lancer's.*

All the brands (both foreign and domestic) listed above are available just about everywhere in the US. Anyone sticking to these tried and true choices is unlikely to go wrong.

General guidelines for businesspeople who want to explore wines without the penalty of serving a really bad bottle to guests:

• Be wary of white wines over three years old and red wines older than five years. They may have turned the corner—become oxidized through age. This warning is particularly important for people living in the Midwest and other parts of the country where wine isn't yet widely drunk. The turnover there is slower than in California and New York, and bottles *stay longer on the shelves. Be careful.* (Top-flight wine, however, requires considerable bottle age before it is ready to drink.)

• Before buying a case (usually 10% cheaper), the invariable rule is to buy a bottle and taste it. Especially important when a local liquor dealer is offering a "special." People who don't trust their own taste shouldn't feel hesitant to ask someone who knows about wine to sample it and give an opinion. The friend or business associate who is asked will be flattered.

• In the long run, the best rule is to seek a dealer who can be trusted and learn to rely on his judgment. In almost every city, there is a liquor store that is trying to build up its wine business. Give it a try. Name or describe a wine that you have enjoyed and ask the dealer to suggest another like it. If he knows his business, he will produce something equally good.

Don't overlook some of the good, inexpensive jug wines produced in this country. Many guests now prefer a glass of chilled white wine as a drink before dinner. Keep a jug of *Gallo Chablis Blanc* or *Sauvignon Blanc* in the refrigerator.

How to deal with sediment in very old red wines: (1) Uncork carefully. (2) Hold neck of bottle over a desk lamp or lit candle while pouring into a clear decanter. Concentrated light from below makes it easy to see when the particles are about to flow. That's the time to stop pouring and discard the remainder.

Best champagne glass: Use tall, slim, fluted or tulip-shaped glasses. (Never fill more than two-thirds of the way.) Common saucer-shaped glass dissipates bubbles too fast. Serve champagne before, during and after dinner as the only drink. Eliminates mixing drinks and selecting wines. Best type: *Vintage Brut.*

Choosing the Right Puppy

Don't buy a puppy on impulse. Buy it from a breeder, if possible, rather than from a pet store. And make the decision carefully.

First consideration: Type of dog is often more important than size. Many large dogs actually need less room than smaller ones. Original function for which the breed was developed often influences temperament.

• *Scent hounds* (beagle, basset, dachshund, bloodhound). Well suited to city living and children.

• *Sight or gaze hounds* (Saluki, Afghan, Irish wolfhound, Scottish deerhound, greyhound). Among the fastest dogs, they were originally bred for running down prey and killing it. They still need lots of room to be happy.

• *Sporting dogs* (spaniels, setters, pointers, retrievers). Originally bred to locate game and retrieve it. Need a little less room than hounds.

But, with the exception of Labrador and Newfoundland retrievers, they are *not* especially protective or good with children.

• *Working dogs* (shepherds, malamutes, huskies, collies, sheepdogs). Probably the most intelligent and protective of all groups. Large (60-150 pounds) and used to outdoor work, but they adapt nicely to city life if exercised twice a day. Actually require *less* space than smaller, more active dogs like terriers.

• *Terriers* (Airedale, Scottish, Welsh, West Highland White, fox, miniature schnauzers). The most alert and active dogs. Also tenacious and often aggressive. Need space. Good with children, whose energy they match. Extremely protective (a benefit for older people, as long as they can cope with the terrier's high level of activity).

• ***Toy dogs* (Pekinese, toy poodle, Yorkshire terrier, Maltese, Italian greyhound, Pomeranian). Originally developed as playthings for royalty and nobility. Charming companions for adults. But strongly *not recommended for small children,* no matter how adorable the puppies and dogs may look. They're much too fragile.**

• *Nonsporting dogs* is a catch-all group with no special characteristics. Includes unrelated breeds, such as the poodle, French and English bulldogs, Boston terrier, chow chow, Dalmatian and Lhasa apso. They tend to be good guard dogs and excellent pets.

Most dog owners strongly prefer one sex over the other. *General pros and cons:*

• *Males* (called *dogs* by breeders) don't get pregnant. They *do* fight, wander, chase cars and display aggressive-dominant behavior toward people.

• *Females (bitches)* are more protective and gentle. They neither wander nor fight, but if they're not spayed, they can become pregnant. Even if they're kept locked up, living through their semiannual heat periods is difficult because of all the unwanted attention from neighboring dogs.

Best to see *both* the pup's parents at the breeder. Chief reason to buy there rather than at a pet store: Not only will buyer see what the puppy will look like as an adult, he will also be able to judge its genetic inheritance by the health of its parents.

Puppies are best chosen—and make the best adjustment to a new home—when they're 6-12 weeks old. At this age, they're so cute that it's hard to choose rationally, even with the knowledge that the choice is one that will have to be lived with for the next 10 or 15 years.

At this age, curiosity is the best indicator of intelligence. Some quick and easy intelligence and temperament tests to help select the best pup of the litter:

Visual tests:

• Shine a pocket flashlight at the pup.
• Show it a mirror.
• Roll a ball toward it.
• Wave a sheet of white paper.
• Drag an object along on a string.

Hearing tests (to be done out of the puppy's sight):

• Blow a police whistle.
• Clap hands.
• Blow a kazoo or noisemaker.

If the pup shows it hears the sound, that's good. If it tries to locate the source, that's excellent.

Body sensitivity is important in training. Gently pinch the puppy's ear between the ball of the thumb and the forefinger. Then push down the puppy's hindquarters, forcing it to sit. Note its reactions. A puppy that doesn't react has little body sensitivity and may be difficult to train because it won't feel corrections. A puppy that whines, cowers or runs away is so sensitive that it will fear corrections and be difficult to train.

Temperament can be tested by seeing the puppy's attitude toward strangers. Jump right in front of the puppy. It should show neither fear nor anger. Surprise followed by friendliness is a good reaction.

If the puppy has all the traits tested for, with love, patience, and training, it should grow up into a wonderful, rewarding dog.

Note: Don't forget local animal shelters as a source of puppies and older dogs. Many of these animals are pedigreed, too.

Choosing a Cat

The first question to answer before choosing a cat can be settled only in your mind: Are you looking for disposition or for exquisiteness? Most people would vote for disposition, and they are right. It is the *most important* consideration in choosing an animal. And the key to disposition and temperament lies in the breed you choose. *Example:* Some big-city dwellers would really prefer a dog. For such people the cat is actually a substitute dog (one that doesn't have to be walked at night). Knowing the breed is the only real assurance of getting a cat whose temperament even approximates the kind you want.

In fact, this assurance is the only advantage of a full-breed cat over the domestic shorthair, better known as the American alley cat. Domestic shorthairs make fine pets and can have wonderful temperaments. However, in choosing from a litter of these you're trusting to luck as to what its temperament will be.

Before Buying

Be sure you're dealing with a store that breeds mainly for disposition. Avoid any store where the emphasis seems to be on the latest fashion in length of tail, head shape, etc.

Next, try to determine which breed suits your taste, your habits and your lifestyle. If, for example, you lead an active life, travel a fair amount, and want a sturdy cat that will become a self-sufficient part of the family, you're better off picking a domestic shorthair.

Shorthair Breeds

• *Domestic shorthairs (the common American alley cat).* These can be wonderful pets, but choose with care. A cute little kitten can grow up to be mean. When you go to the pound or Humane Society, choose a cat that's past the kitten stage or older—one that comes running to you, purrs, and rubs against the cage. Then you'll be getting a wonderful, affectionate pet. (You'll also be doing a good deed by giving an older animal a home.)

• *Burmese.* These are known as the dogs of the cat family, and for good reason. They are probably the most affectionate of all cats. There is no such thing, in the mind of a Burmese, as too much love. As in all things, there are always exceptions to the rule. However, if you want to be overwhelmed with demonstrations of affection, your best bet is a Burmese.

• *Siamese.* These are the perfect, all-round cats, spunky, affectionate and bright. (They used to have a bad press, some of it deserved, that painted them as aloof and mean. This was caused partly by overbreeding, which is usually avoided now.) They do have a fairly compelling voice, which they use a lot, and this irritates some people. So if you want a cat that's going to be seen but not heard, *don't* get a Siamese. Otherwise, they are perfect cats and will fit into any normal, animal-loving family.

• *Tonkinese.* A cross between the Burmese and the Siamese, these combine the best of both breeds. They are almost as affectionate as the full Burmese and have the added spunk of the Siamese. The feature that may distinguish them from either is their sense of humor.

• *Abyssinian.* These are very active cats, with almost no voice. They have the rare coloration of wild creatures. The Abyssinian is the status symbol for people who hate status symbols. To the superficial observer, these cats may not seem particularly affectionate or people-centered because of their high activity level. This is an illusion. It is just that their major preoccupations—moving, chasing flies, etc.—may make them take less kindly than other shorthair breeds to being held and cuddled. They *are* affectionate. This breed, however, is not the best choice for a family whose small child wants to carry the kitty around all day.

• *Russian Blue.* (They're really a sort of gray, though you'd be drummed out of all cat associations for saying so.) These are the intellectuals of the cat family—the thinkers and the problem solvers. They don't sell themselves well in cages precisely because they sit there looking like wise old men and won't do cute tricks. Just get them home, though, and watch them figure things out. Because of their intelligence, they're also extraordinarily trainable. Just say to a Russian Blue kitten, "I'd rather you didn't scratch that chair, please," and you can practically hear it reply, "Oh sorry—I get it."

Longhair Cats

• *Maine coon cat.* These excellent pets get to be *very* big (weighing as much as 20-30 pounds). They are nice-tempered animals that can be relied upon to sit around all day exuding good will. If your other pets are neurotic, a Maine coon cat is a good addition, one that will exert a beneficial psychological influence.

• *Persian.* The theory is that the main job of Persian cats is to sit around looking gorgeous, and that they are not quite as bright as the shorthair breeds. Much is unfair in this notion. Considerable numbers of Persians are bright and spunky, in addition to being gorgeous. For people who put a prime value on pure elegance, the Persian is, of course, the cat of choice.

• *Himalayan.* This cross between the Persian and the Siamese has been credited with being slightly brainier than Persians.

Cats and Allergies

Contrary to general belief, people with allergies *can* have cats. Some people will be allergic to one cat but *not* to another (even within the same litter) or allergic to longhairs but not to shorthairs. To find out if you are allergic, hold the cat and see if you swell up, sneeze or exhibit other allergic symptoms.

Cats and the Traveling Family

Some cats stand up better than others to being left alone a lot. Those that best stand up to this treatment are the less affectionate breeds. Really affectionate cats will suffer. The best way to handle this problem, for all cats, is to get a second one. *One* cat shouldn't be left alone for days, or even a weekend, even if someone comes in to feed it and give it water. *Two* cats, however, can stand up to this quite well, especially if they like each other.

Cats and Their Habitat

Cats are true conservatives. They like the status to remain quo. They do *not* want to go any place new—ever. If you feel sorry for your cat because it never gets to leave the apartment, you're wasting your pity. Cats love their own good homes and see no need to try to improve on them.

If you're a weekend traveler who goes to a different place every weekend, *don't* take the cat. It will be unhappy. If, however, you go away to the *same* place every weekend, and you want to take the cat, that's another matter. In that case, the cat thinks, "Oh, every Friday we go to my other house."

Precautions When Buying a Cat

• Don't bring your young child along to help you choose. Children usually want the first cat they see.

• Don't pick the cat (or any pet) for the purpose of teaching a child "responsibility" or presume that caring for the animal will help "build character." It won't—and it's not fair to impose such burdens on either the child or the animal. Care of the cat is *your* responsibility.

• Don't buy two cats at the *same* time or they'll relate more to *each other* than to you. Take some time to train your first cat (a few weeks or a month) . . . and teach it the rules of the house. Then you can get a second cat. You may have to deal with a few days of jealousy from the first cat, but you'll at least have two cats that rely first on *you* and then on each other. *Bonus:* The first cat will teach the second the rules of the house.

Source: Roz Riddle, owner of Fabulous Felines, 657 Second Ave., New York 10016, and author of *The City Cat.*

How to Buy Caviar

Caviar from sturgeon is top of the line and most expensive. Three grades (beluga, osetra, sevruga) all come from the same fish. Beluga is biggest grained and most expensive; color is black or gray. Osetra grains cost somewhat less and are almost the same size, brown to golden in color. Sevruga grains are much smaller and least expensive.

Freshest, best caviar is packed with *mild* salt, labeled *Malossol.* So is *pressed caviar,* which is top-grade caviar, too "ripe" to pack in whole grains. A best buy, it is very rich tasting, authentic (served widely in Russia), and, unlike whole-grain, can be stored in a freezer. *Bottom of the line:* Strongly salted caviar that is sold in jars.

How to serve: Figure ¾ of an ounce per person. Serve whole-grain right out of the tin atop crushed ice, pressed caviar at room temperature. Surround both with small plates of lemon wedges, chopped onions, chopped egg whites, chopped yolks. Spoon some caviar onto thin-sliced black bread, toast or thin pancakes *(blinis)* and let guests add whatever they want (nothing is necessary).

Don't shun red-colored salmon caviar, which is delicious and far less expensive. Best tasting are the smaller-size grains from *silver salmon* (rather than more common *Ketovya* or *chum salmon* caviar which is often artificially colored).

Antique Auction Do's and Don'ts

• Examine the items carefully at the pre-sale exhibition. (Take along a tape measure and flashlight.) Beware of wooden furniture with legs made of wood that differs from the surface. Chances are someone has put the piece together from two or more pieces.

• When an item catches your interest, ask the attendant what price it is likely to bring—usually a pretty good estimate.

• If you can narrow your choice down to one item of each type, you don't have to attend the auction. Simply decide on the maximum you are willing to pay and place the bid in advance. If a piece isn't bid up to your price, the auctioneer will award it to you at the *next level of bidding.*

Example: If your bid was $250 but the bidding stopped at $175, you will get the piece for $200.

On the other hand, if you cannot narrow your choice down to one item of each type and you must be physically present at the auction, find out what time the first item on your list will go on the block. *Rule of thumb:* Most auctions clip along at about 100 items an hour. Hence, if you are planning to bid on Lot 121, you can arrive an hour after the auction is scheduled to begin.

• *Antique* means that an object is 100 years old or older.

• Buyers do best in June, July, August and December, which are slow months at most auction houses.

• Auctioneers never take anything back. They are not responsible for bidders' errors. If in doubt, bring an expert along.

• Don't be overeager. It encourages bids from "phantom" buyers, bidding you up. Best not to open the bidding.

• Don't worry about bidding against dealers. They have to buy low enough to handle their overhead and make a profit.

For Art Collectors

When to buy art: Year-end is worst time to buy from a dealer. *Best time:* May and June, when dealers seek to wind down inventory for the end of the business year. In the summer, many dealers travel to Europe on buying trips or go on vacation. They would prefer to have sold most or all of their art before departing. As a result, they are likely to be more receptive to lower offers from collectors than they would be otherwise. Be prepared to pay immediately upon acceptance of offer.

• Beware of art print stores and galleries that promise appreciation in value. Over 90% of art sold *depreciates*—quickly.

• Get out of an art field when it hits the front pages. The peak has arrived.

• Stay up to date on the art market by subscribing to *ARTnewsletter* (5 W. 37 St., New York 10018). Gives sale prices—and tells which paintings don't sell.

Stereo Savvy

Reduce tape hiss by recording at a high volume . . . just short of distortion. Before recording on a new cassette, rewind it once to settle the tape on the spools. Avoid "rumble" by placing a standard red rubber eraser between the dust cover and turntable; vibrations will escape instead of feeding back through the needle.

Stereo Speaker Placement

(1) Small speakers can supply richer bass if moved to the corners of the room. Large speakers may sound too booming if put in corners. (2) Small speakers may give better stereo imaging when raised from the floor. (3) Never face speakers toward a smooth plaster wall or picture window. A hard surface bounces the sound back and makes the music shrill. (4) To be sure the speakers are "in phase," switch to monaural mode and stand midway between them. Shift your head from side to side. If the sound doesn't seem to come from exactly halfway between the speakers, they're out of phase. *Solution:* Reverse the wires at the rear of *one* speaker.

Buying a Stereo Cabinet

(1) Omit the casters on tall cabinets. They shouldn't be moved when full because they're top-heavy. (2) Look for a hinged glass or acrylic top to serve as a dust cover for your turntable. (3) Insist on adjustable shelves, so you can tailor space to your components. (4) Be sure there are holes in the back panel for ventilation and for threading wires through.

How to Talk to Computer Salespeople

Inexperienced shoppers often feel overwhelmed by technical details when they shop for a personal computer. Some things to know:

- Expansion. The ability of the basic computer to accept additional hardware in the form of specialized circuit boards, terminals, storage capacity, or peripherals.
- Upgrading. Once expansion limits are reached, are the terminals, software, and peripheral equipment compatible with more powerful models?
- Word length and bits. The bit is the smallest unit of information the computer can recognize. Word length refers to the number of bits that can be handled in a single operation. The longer the word length, the faster and more expensive the equipment will be. A 16-bit word length has become the minimum for most business uses.
- Memory size. The main random-access memory (RAM) stores the computer's active memory—programs and data. It is emptied when the computer is turned off. A good computer for home or office needs at least 128K (128,000) bytes (eight bits equal a byte). This can be enlarged by adding memory chips and extended memory boards. Auxiliary memory storage devices form a permanent memory. These devices are called floppy or hard disks. The type and size of the disk storage system is dictated by needs. A 5½-inch floppy disk holds 360K. A hard disk can store upwards of 40 megabytes (one megabyte equals a million bytes).
- Ruggedness. Is the chassis sturdy? Are the circuit boards easy to remove for servicing? Do the exterior panels protect against spills and dust?
- Terminals. These are the television-like devices on which information is displayed. Cathode-ray-tube models are the best. The display panel should be large enough to show 24 lines of 80 characters each. (Five-inch models are impractical for anything but hobby use.) The keyboard through which the user can change the copy should be set up the same as a regular typewriter. A separate calculator-style keyboard speeds numerical entries.

Computer Cautions

- Computer insurance trap. Personal computers kept and used at home *for business* aren't covered by homeowner's insurance. (PCs used only for personal use *are* covered by homeowner's policies.) If the home computer is written off as a business expense, special computer insurance is needed.
- Extended warranties on personal computers make sense only if they cover the printer, keyboard and disk drive. If the policy covers just the computer, it's probably not worth the investment. *Reason:* A computer's central processing unit has few moving parts. It's the other components that are more likely to break down.

Choosing Computer Camp for Child

More than 100 summer camps now feature computer instruction as their primary dedication, and many other camps have added computer courses to their mix of activities. Sleep-away programs run $200–$500 per week. Day camps that use the facilities of colleges or high schools are considerably less expensive.

You first should ask of a computer camp what you would expect of any summer camp—responsible counselors, decent hygiene and medical care, a warm atmosphere and well-supervised activities. For a young beginner, look for a camp with other activities your child likes as well as computer work. Does the camp teach children to *use* computers (fine for beginners) or to *program* them (a must for more experienced youngsters)?

Computer Questions to Ask

What is the ratio of computers to campers? One-to-one is best; two-to-one is acceptable. Anything less is not satisfactory for the really committed child.

What brands of computers does the camp use? Are they compatible with the equipment at your child's school or at home? For elementary-age youngsters, switching brands can be very confusing and difficult.

For more experienced children, a central mainframe computer wth a number of workstations or terminals offers more versatility and power than independent microcomputers.

For computer whizzes there are intensive camps that give the youngsters up to nine hours of computer time a day. Programs such as the Duke University Computer Camp or the University of Missouri Computer Science Institute are not appropriate for every child.

Computer camps serve young people ages 10–17. The American Camping Association publishes a guide to more than 90 such camps. If you send the association a list of requirements that you feel are important for your child, it will send you both the guide and a selection of camps that seem most suitable. *Cost:* $15.

Source: *1984 Parents' Guide to Accredited Camps,* American Camping Association, 335 E. 46 St., New York, 10017.

Coaching for College Entrance Exams

Is coaching for the SAT test worth it? Even the lowest estimate cites average gains of 34 points. Some reputable schools are reporting increases of up to 100 points. Reasoning and problem-solving skills *are* coachable. *Before spending the money (up to $375):* Check out the school. The course should include at least 30–40 hours of in-class instruction spread over 6–12 sessions, small classes and up-to-date materials. Coaching is particularly valuable if your son or daughter: (1) Is a newcomer to the tests. (2) Tends to become nervous during exams. (3) Wants to go to a highly selective college.

Buying Kitchen Knives

Stick to blades made from *high-carbon stainless steel.* It's the only material that holds a sharp edge *and* resists rust and stains. Make sure the handle is attached with rivets, *not* adhesive. Never put knives in the dishwasher, no matter what the manufacturer says. Wipe the blade and handle clean and store in a knife rack. Keep knives sharpened. *Dull* blades cause accidents.

How Utility Meters Work

Both electric and gas meters operate on the same principle. Each has several dials with pointers that tell you how much of the product you are using.

Electric meter:

It has five numbered dials. The pointers on three of the dials turn clockwise, while the other two go counterclockwise.

It is read from left to right. The pointer always registers the number it has just passed. Example: If the pointer rests between three and four read the number as three. This holds true even if the pointer is touching the four but has not gone past it.

The numbers taken off of each of the dials gives you the reading of the meter at that moment. When it is read again (usually in a month), you know how many kilowatt-hours of electricty have been consumed.

Meters can be wrong. Electric meters can wear out or be damaged during an electrical storm. A dramatic increase in your electric bill should signal a call to the utility company.

Gas meter: It is read exactly the same way as the electric meter. Difference: It has four dials. The pointers of two turn clockwise, while the other two go counterclockwise.

Insurance Policies You Only *Think* You Need

Avoid special policies for cancer or other diseases and mail-order hospitalization plans. The payout on such plans is typically just 50¢ of each premium dollar —or less.

Credit Life Insurance. This is a very poor bet unless you are quite old or in poor health.

Auto Rental Insurance. Only on an icy night in a strange town when you have had a few drinks might this coverage be worth the price. *(Best:* Don't drive at all.) Otherwise, about $4 of each $5-a-day you pay goes not to insurance but to the rental company's expenses and profits.

Source: Andrew Tobias, author of *The Invisible Bankers: Everything the Insurance Industry Never Wanted You to Know,* The Linden Press, 1230 Ave. of the Americas, New York 10020.

What Supermarkets Don't Tell You

Supermarkets usually place the most expensive items at eye level, where they are more likely to be selected on impulse. *Recommended:* Look at the entire group of products before deciding on a purchase, unless you have a preference for a specfic brand.

Generic items can offer real savings, but quality varies widely. *Best bets:* Products such as household bleach, which, by law, must contain specific ingredients common to all brands. *Trap:* House brands and national brands may actually be cheaper, when on sale, than generic brands. *Point:* Comparison shop.

Bargaining With a Shopkeeper

Getting a better price can be rewarding economically and psychologically. How to do it successfully:

Be discreet. A shopkeeper won't reduce a price if he's worried that the special value will be made public.

Confine most bargaining to the privately owned shops. However, don't write off supermarkets and department stores. Occasionally, managers of these stores will bargain, especially on slightly damaged merchandise or goods that are older and hard to dispose of.

Make it clear to the shopkeeper that you are a serious shopper who intends to spend money. Select several definite articles and several tentative purchases. Ask the shopkeeper for the total cost before writing the bill. As he completes his tally, begin some tongue-clucking and head-shaking. Then, softly ask the merchant if that price is the best he can do.

If he says it is, bargain by offering to pay in cash. This method usually works only if the purchase price exceeds $100.

If the shopkeeper still refuses to bargain, leave everything on the counter and begin to walk out, slowly; this ploy may prompt him to reconsider. However, less hard-core bargainers may wish to buy a few of the items anyway and leave the bargaining at that.

Source: *A Shopping Guide to the Lower East Side,* by Ellen Telzer and Sharon Greene, 2 Grace Court, Brooklyn, NY 11201.

Cancelled Check is Proof that Fire Insurance is Paid For, Right? Wrong

Fire and casualty policies should be in hand (on file) before the full premium is paid. One firm, after finding its plant burned to the ground, didn't have the policy it had paid for. Though it produced the canceled check to the broker, its claim was disallowed. The wise course is to buy insurance as you would an automobile: Give the broker a small deposit, but don't pay up until the policy is delivered.

Tipoff That Phone Bill is Incorrect

Calls listed *without* a time or with the digits missing (5 P.M., instead of 5:00 P.M.) more often than not have been misbilled.

Source: Alan H. Jordan, telemarketing consultant, Wayne, Pa, writing in *The Office,* 1200 Summer St., Stamford, CT 06904, monthly.

Mistakes When Filing Insurance Claims

Failure to accurately calculate losses. It's hard to believe, but many people can't accurately determine their losses—whether by damage or theft. *Reason:* They fail to maintain effective accounting and record-retention procedures to document the losses. It's not uncommon to hear of a situation where a theft loss amounted to $250,000, but the claimant could only substantiate $100,000 of the loss. It's important to plan ahead with your accountant to determine the best procedures for demonstrating what you own, should you have to make a claim.

Overstating the loss. This is a subtle problem. If a claimant purposely overstates the loss to the point where the insurance company could question his integrity, the latter will take a hard line. Generally, if the claimant takes a fair position, the insurer will still bargain over the loss claim but will be more reasonable.

Underestimating the loss. This sounds like a contradiction of the above, but it's not. Immediately after losses are claimed, adjuster will ask claimant for an *estimate* of the damage, *not* an accurate, justified number. The insurer requires such a rough estimate, but be wary of providing a number before taking time to get a reliable estimate. If the adjuster reports a number that's too low and then must go back later to the insurer and restate it much higher, his credibility and yours are hurt. He looks foolish. Those hurt feelings can make future loss negotiations tricky. So tell the adjuster about any problems in coming up with a number.

How to Collect From Insurance Companies

In many situations, you can negotiate successfully with an insurance company *without* retaining a lawyer. It is important to know *when* to negotiate yourself and *how* to negotiate *effectively.*

Where to Start

Your *insurance agent,* if he is *not* an employee of the insurer, should be your first line of inquiry. An independent agent is better able to assist in obtaining the full amount to which you are entitled. A good relationship with clients is what keeps him in business.

He will often present your claim, negotiate it and obtain a satisfactory settlement for you without charge. He's especially valuable on smaller claims. Also, if you negotiate yourself, he can be a major source of information and advice.

Should You Hire a Lawyer?

The major deciding factor is economic. On small claims, a lawyer's fee might be prohibitive, but on larger claims you could lose money by negotiating with an insurance company yourself.

In some cases, you might simply pay a flat fee for the attorney's review of your claim. Initial consultation will usually provide you with helpful information and assist the attorney in deciding whether or not it will pay for him to take your case.

Other considerations:

• *Subjective factors.* If you don't feel comfortable retaining a lawyer, go it alone.

• *No-fault versus at-fault states.* Negotiating your own claim makes a lot more sense in a no-fault state, where the insurance company is bound by law to reimburse you for your losses. But even in a no-fault state, or if you don't apply in time for all of the benefits to which you were entitled, your claim may not be honored if the forms are presented incorrectly.

• *Language.* Understanding the convoluted terminology used in insurance policies and law is a major stumbling block for the layman. To negotiate successfully, you must be comfortable with the language.

• *Reputation.* Some insurance companies deal fairly and quickly. Others are notoriously difficult and slow. Ask your insurance agent or a negligence attorney about the company you are dealing with. You may need legal help to negotiate a favorable settlement with a difficult company.

• *Pain and suffering.* When multiples of out-of-pocket expenses are involved due to pain and suffering, it is best to hire a lawyer. Lawyers can point out losses you have not even thought of. Also, the insurance company will take into account what you are saving by not hiring a lawyer and offer you less.

If You Go it Alone

• *Read the policy very carefully.* Pay special attention to exclusions and coverages. Before presenting your claim, take a close look at the policy. Make sure you're presenting it in a way that makes it *evident* that your claim is covered. (If you can't find your policy, the insurer is obligated to give you a copy.)

• *Document everything completely.* It is the *most important* part of an insurance claim. Support *every* aspect of your claim, including doctor bills, receipts for medicines, transportation for medical reasons and a letter from your employer stating lost wages. *Think of everything.* Witnessing an injury to a loved one may cause compensable emotional trauma. A husband (wife) may recover for the lost services and companionship of his (her) injured spouse.

• *Find out what your claim is worth.* Ask your insurance agent or a negligence lawyer what a reasonable offer would be in your situation.

• *Be prepared to take a discount.* There has to be a motivation for the insurer to settle a claim. One advantage of negotiating without a lawyer is that a quick settlement may be offered to avoid legal expenses. So decide *what amount you are willing to settle for.* The settlement offer will depend on various factors, including clarity, proof of coverage, damages, documentation, how likely you are to prevail at trial and the caseload of the court you would have to sue in. (Some insurers offer nothing until the trial date.)

Bodily Injury

Claims for bodily injury can be the most complicated and negotiable, especially when based upon pain and suffering.

• *In a no-fault state,* you are limited to out-of-pocket expenses in a nonserious injury. This includes lost wages. In a fault-governed state, you can negotiate for more.

• *Don't miss damages.* Start at the top of your head and go down to your toes, to include *every* part that's been hurt.

• *Photograph your injury.* In addition to medical reports, photos are the best documentation of suffering.

• *Consider every aspect* of your life affected by your injury. Include your career, sports, hobbies, future interests and family relationships.

• *Ask what a lawyer would ask*—at least *twice* the actual expense when there has been no permanent disability. Where liability is clear, the insurance company will be likely to give you what you ask, if they believe that you really had difficulties and were out of work for a few weeks. However, where there has been permanent disability, multiples of expenses do not apply. *Example:* Your medical bills for a lost eye might have been only $3,000, but a jury might award you 50 times that amount.

If You Cannot Reach a Settlement

An insurance company has a *fiduciary duty* (a relationship based on trust, like that with your lawyer or stockbroker) to deal fairly and in good faith with its insured. *What to do if you are not treated well:*

• If you feel that the company is either unreasonably delaying your claim or acting in bad faith, make a complaint to your state insurance regulatory agency. In most cases, the agency will write a letter to the company.

• If your time is being wasted by the insurance company's bureaucracy, the small claims court may be appropriate. Such action will pressure the company to settle with you more quickly on your terms.

• Many states have laws penalizing an insurer for bad faith. If you feel the company has been acting in bad faith, you can initiate a lawsuit and possibly collect a multiple of your claim in punitive damages.

Source: Dan Brecher, an attorney at 230 Park Ave., New York 10169. He has extensive experience in negotiating with insurance companies.

When to Sue an Attorney for Malpractice

The legal profession is now entering its own malpractice crisis. The number of suits against attorneys brought by clients is increasing and the availability of malpractice insurance is decreasing.

Ground rules for considering a suit against your lawyer:

• Where malpractice is charged in connection with litigation, the client must show that the litigation would have ended with a result more favorable to the client except for the attorney's neglect.

• Where the attorney fell below the standards of skill and knowledge ordinarily possessed by attorneys under similar circumstances. Expert testimony is needed to support this charge. And the standard may be affected by specialization (which raises the standard of care required), custom and the locality. Locality and custom can't lower the standard, but they may be used in defense to show that the procedure or the law involved is unsettled.

Best way to avoid malpractice charges (and costs of a suit):

• Good communication between lawyer and client.

• Avoid creating a situation where lawyer is handling serious matters for personal friends. The tendency is to deal with them on a more casual basis.

• The attorney should give an honest opinion of each case, good or bad. Client shouldn't press him for a guarantee as to the result and for a value on the claim.

• *All* fee arrangements should be in writing.

• The attorney should spell out the scope of his responsibilities, including appeals, and a limit should be placed on costs.

• The agreement should provide for periodic payments unless the matter is one involving a contingent fee, and for withdrawal, if there is a default in payment.

Career Skills

How to Prepare a Speech

Decide exactly and precisely what your subject is. Then logically think through your subject. List the ideas and conclusions to stress. Become thoroughly familiar with the important books, speeches and other literature on the subject.

Prepare an outline of the speech: Introduction, main body (usually divided up into two or four sections) and the conclusion.

Start by *writing* the speech. Be complete.

Prepare a brief introduction. Various ways in which you can introduce your speech: (1) Attack the topic head-on by simply announcing it. (2) Begin with a human interest story, an illustration or a funny anecdote relevant to the topic. (3) Startle the audience by beginning with an exciting question or an arousing statement. (4) Use a quote or an idea from somebody else. (5) Explain in factual terms why the topic is important to your audience.

The main body of the speech should make it apparent to your audience that you have a thorough knowledge of the topic. Back up your points with facts, numbers, examples. If you want to convince your audience of the wisdom of your view on the topic, begin with material that agrees with those views. Don't argue. Just explain your points. Those points should be clearly defined either at the beginning or the end of the speech, or as they develop within the speech, or any combination of those three.

Conclude: Briefly go over the points you've made. Use a quote. Strive for a big climax. You can compliment the audience. Or end by being encouraging and optimistic, or by telling a particularly dramatic story, an historical anecdote or a joke. You can also recommend that your audience take some action. Another ending would be to suggest that they change their view to yours.

- Type the last line of each page on the top of the next page.
- Don't have speech typed in all capital letters. Word recognition is easier when normal upper- and lower-case letters are used.
- Have speech typed triple-spaced.
- Don't hyphenate words.
- When gesturing, keep a finger (or pencil) on the line being read (so place won't be lost). Gesture with other hand.
- Don't staple speech manuscript. Allow completed pages or large cards to be casually (and noiselessly) slid off to side.
- Memorize important points. Then eyes can lift from text to look directly at audience when these points are being made. Memorize both opening and closing lines.
- Use a *slant*-top lectern so manuscript can be read by dropping eyes only slightly—but not your head.
- Write words "slow down" in large letters at top of *each* page. That compensates for general tendency to speak too rapidly.
- Speaker who writes on blackboard or easel pad as a visual aid should keep it on his *left* (when he's facing the audience) if he's right handed, and on his right if he's left-handed. Prevents turning back on audience or blocking what's written.
- When your remarks are scheduled for the *end* of a program, have two versions ready: One regular length and the other much shorter. If the program runs long, go with the short one.
- Most people speak several tones too high. *The reason:* They don't hear their voice as others do. The sound reaches them through the head rather than through vibrations in the air, distorting the tone. Speak low. Use lots of jaw and lip movement. This will improve tone, make you look more animated and slow your delivery, giving you more time to think of what you want to say.
- **Prespeech stage fright can be turned into a vitalizing force with exercises that actors do in private, just before going on: Flop hands and legs, and roll head and shoulders . . . stretch facial muscles (shut eyes tightly, with nose and mouth practically touching, then release into a silent scream with eyes and mouth wide open). . .finish by stretching while walking (big, indulgent, lion-like movements). Then face the crowd energized and free from tension.**

How to Be Better at Math

A surprisingly large number of adults, including many business people, have a secret fear of numbers. When they have to analyze budget figures, or even calculate a restaurant tip, they react with confusion or panic.

Symptoms of adult math anxiety: Going blank when figures are discussed. Blurring together numbers printed on a page. Forgetting basic math procedures.

Typical results: Avoid tasks or even whole fields of endeavor that depend on math. Buck-passing or stalling on math-dependent decisions. Failing to question suspicious numbers.

To solve the problem: Dispel myths that math is a

rigid discipline or that some people just naturally lack math ability. *Reality:* In many cases, approximate figures will do. Even those not well schooled in math can catch up quickly with proper instruction.

Recommended:

• Always write down figures when they come up in discussions.

• Ask questions if something is unclear. (If others are silent, chances are they are confused, too.)

• Estimate and round off numbers whenever possible.

Work on math problems alone whenever possible. Review the basics that are vital in business: decimals, fractions and percentages. A good review book is *Quick Arithmetic* by R.A. and M.J. Carman (John Wiley & Sons).

Especially useful for the math anxious: *Overcoming Math Anxiety* by Shelia Tobias (Houghton Mifflin) and *Mind Over Math* by Dr. Stanley Kogelman and Dr. Joseph Warren (McGraw-Hill).

Source: Dr. Stanley Kogelman, director, Mind Over Math, treatment service, Bayside, NY, and Bonnie Donady, counselor, Wesleyan University Mathematics Clinic, Middletown, Conn.

Sounding Better on the Phone

• Make a better impression on the phone by opening your mouth wider as you speak and moving your lips. Most people move their lips too little, flattening the voice tone. Do not squeeze the phone between your neck and shoulder. This tenses your throat and makes you talk from one side of your mouth.

• Speak in your lower vocal range. Telephones transmit lower pitches more truly than high ones.

Time Savers

• To get off the phone fast, get a clue to other person's activity *early* in a conversation and use it to *close. Example:* "Did I interrupt you?" might bring a response, "No. Just going over some budget figures." Then conversation can be ended with, "OK, I'll let you get back to your budget."

• When calling long-winded party, time call for just before he goes out to lunch or leaves for the day. Give *him* a reason to keep call short without offending him.

• When asking someone to call back later, suggest best time to call. Avoids repeated interruptions at inconvenient moments.

• Never hold the phone waiting for someone who's on another line. Request an immediate callback instead.

• Make phone calls before 9 a.m. or after 3 p.m. At other hours, too many people are in meetings.

• Don't return all calls the minute you get back to the office. Spot the crucial ones. Half the rest will be from people who've already solved their problems; the rest will be back to you soon enough.

• Use a time reminder device to limit length of conversations. (Often "politically" desirable to look annoyed when it goes off.)

• **Set some appointments at odd times instead of on the hour or half hour. Meeting at 2:50 or 3:20 makes others more prompt and puts across the message of careful time management.**

• Accumulate quick, easy, yes/no type work in a special "children's hour" folder. Set aside odd periods to work on it (while waiting for a meeting to start, while waiting in airport, while riding on commuter train).

• To find your coat fast on a crowded rack. Tuck one sleeve over a hanger bar. To spot your car quickly in a crowded parking lot, mark antenna with brightly colored tape.

Getting Ready for a Job Interview

A job interview is like a game. It has rules, and the participants have roles to play. What you can win is an offer. What the interviewer can win is the proper person for the job.

Your role as interviewee is to play the confident applicant who can project talent, willingness and suitability for the opening. If you have done your homework, you should have no problem. *What to do:*

• Spend the morning in the library researching the company, or talk to friends who know similar organizations.

• Interview yourself on a tape recorder until you hear confidence in your answers to questions.

• **Prepare positive answers to potentially difficult queries like, "I'm a little worried about your lack of experience . . ." or, "You've been out of work a long time, haven't you?"**

Interviewers play one of four general roles:

• The target-directed interviewer is direct, businesslike and a little impersonal. Respond in kind.

• The all-in-the-family interviewer is warm, friendly and company oriented. Emphasize your team-player attributes.

• The thinking person's interviewer is interested in how you did things or intend to do things. Give logical expanded answers about your methods and theories.

• The make-it-easy-for-me interviewer is unpredictable and prone to snap judgments. Be a responsive audience and let the interviewer keep center stage.

Source: Robert Half, president, Robert Half International, Inc., New York City, and author of *The Robert Half Way to Get Hired in Today's Job Market,* Rawson Wade.

Talking Salary

Guidelines for salary negotiations when job discussions get down to the nitty-gritty:

• Try not to specify a figure. (It will inevitably be lowered.) Get the other person to mention one first.

• Evade the question. If you are asked what you made at your last job, say: That salary is not especially relevant because the job I was doing was very different from what I'll be doing now. Perhaps if you could tell me what the salary range is, I could say whether it seems appropriate.

• Ask the salary range of workers reporting to you if the company has no established salary range.

• Establish the value of benefits before agreeing on a salary figure.

• Ask for a performance and salary review in six months.

What to Leave Out of Your Resume

The style used for writing resumes has changed over the last few years to make them more persuasive and concise. *Goal:* Each resume entry should convince readers that they should hire the writer. *What to omit:*

Photos. A picture may let employers form misleading impressions.

Salary requirements. Why should applicants price themselves out of a job or show that they are a bargain?

Reasons for leaving jobs. These are better explained in interviews.

Date of resume preparation or date available to begin work. Both indicate how long you have been looking for a job. Exception: When looking for seasonal work.

References or a statement that references are available on request. Instead: List them on a separate sheet and adapt them to each individual employment situation.

Empty assurances. All applicants think they are good, honest, loyal and healthy workers. Demonstrate these qualities through concrete examples during interviews.

Vague references to time gaps. Employers look for holes. Explain them in terms of accomplishments. Example: Travel to improve a language capability or research a specific project. *Caution:* Never claim to have been a consultant without proof.

Hobbies and outside interests. Exception: Those that relate to professional interests or show traits that an employer wants. Avoid listing any dangerous or time-consuming activities.

Source: *Resumes: The Nitty Gritty,* by Joyce Lain Kennedy, Suburban Features Inc., Cardiff, Calif.

When You're Interviewed on the Air

• Set the tone right away. Explain at the outset why subject is important.

• Don't stray from the subject.

• Keep answers tight. Allow time for more questions and answers, and thus more information.

• On television, don't look at the cameras. People are more effective when looking directly at show host.

• On radio, sit close to the microphone. The audience will lose much of what you're saying if you're too far away.

Source: Richard Goldberg, president, *You're On,* Visual Communications Consulting, Brighton, Mass.

Secrets of a Successful Inventor

There probably doesn't exist a businessperson who, at one time or another, hasn't thought of an invention he or she thinks is worthy of patenting. Most businesspeople find excuses to delay, many only to see their idea marketed by someone else years later.

Dr. Craven Kurz wasn't willing to suffer that fate. In the last 13 years, the California orthodontist has patented nearly four dozen inventions, including a water distiller, a collapsible toothbrush, a nonlethal weapon... and invisible tooth braces that may well become the standard in a few years. As Kurz's story shows, the route from idea to royalty check is filled with faith, surprises and unexpected success.

A few years ago, I was doing dental work for a lot of Playboy Club bunnies in Los Angeles, and one of the women came to me with a bad bite problem. But since she wanted to do some modeling, she asked for invisible braces. Unfortunately, the item didn't exist. Then a few days later, when I was driving down the freeway, I asked myself why I couldn't put braces on the *back* of her teeth.

It sounded like a good idea, but I assumed that if it was feasible, it would have been done already. That's a trap. *Lesson:* Never assume that what's obvious to you is apparent to others.

Surprises en Route

Fortunately, I did some research and discovered that no one had written about putting braces on the back of teeth. Then I retained a patent attorney to research patents in the field. When the attorney found that there weren't any, that's when I went to work. A good patent attorney is a *must* for any serious inventor. It's even better if that attorney is experienced in your specific field.

I got a surprise when I filed my application at the Patent & Trademark Office. Just as invisible braces had seemed obvious to me, they seemed so recognizable to the patent officers that they rejected the application. So I decided to go to Washington and talk with the officers myself. Contrary to what I expected, they were people, not robots.

I said, hell, if the braces are so obvious, why hasn't someone come up with them before? Finally, after several visits to the Patent Office with my attorney, I was able to convince them to consider the application.

Then the patent official asked for revisions and clarifications. Because of my lack of experience in this area and the time-consuming nature of the bureaucracy, each revision took several months. There were times when I almost wanted to junk the whole project, but slowly I could see the light at the end of the tunnel. Eventually, the last revision was made and the patent finally granted in 1982—six years after the original application.

Fortunately, you don't have to wait until the patent is granted to start marketing it. As long as the Patent Office agrees to consider it, you can market a product on a patent-pending basis.

Inventors should approach companies as soon as the patent is considered. Companies are much more receptive to inventors than you might think. *Strategy:* Send a concise letter to the head of an appropriate manufacturer's research and development office.

Marketing Techniques

I was shocked to find that R&D departments rely on outside innovation as much as they do. In fact, since R&D managers are working for a salary, they instinctively don't take chances themselves.

Once a company is interested in a product, it sends you a disclosure form that legally binds it not to benefit from your invention until a contract is signed. Many unsophisticated inventors fear that companies will steal their ideas. That usually doesn't happen because companies can't afford to get a bad reputation.

In negotiating, the inventor's trump card is his reputation. No matter how good an invention might look, companies are simply more interested in working with an inventor who has already been successful *even if in another field.*

Few things are more satisfying for an inventor than walking away from a company with a contract in hand. But many innovators make the mistake of thinking they'll negotiate for millions of dollars. That almost never happens. Royalties are usually in the 2%–5% range, and maybe 10% if the product is a big-ticket, specialty item like a medical advance. *Advice:* For big profits, inventors should aim for the consumer field. Royalties are low, but sales can be enormous.

Ironically, what holds many people back from making inventions is that they're too close to their work. They can't stand back and see the big picture that encompasses the marketplace. You can almost say that the more training people have in a field, the less inventive they are in that area. They're too wrapped up trying to perfect the procedures they're trained to perform.

When Applying For a Patent

- Expect the Patent & Trademark Office to reject the application at first. It's programmed to say *no.*
- Go over the first and subsequent application in minute detail with both your lawyer and the artist who is needed to provide detailed drawings of either the product or process.
- Educate your lawyer and artists so that the they know as much about your invention as you do. Otherwise, they're likely to make mistakes that can undermine the application.
- Remember that the only things that impress the Patent Office are your ability and knowledge.
- **Be prepared for a long, long wait before a patent is granted. You'll be answering questions and revising the application for years. It takes an immense amount of faith in an invention to stick with it all that time. Most patents don't require six years, but two or three years is a normal period.**

Source: Dr. Craven Kurz, DDS, N. Roxbury Dr., Beverly Hills, Calif. 90210.

Easy Ways to Do Hard Things

• *Skin caught in zipper.* The best and easiest way out is to attack the zipper glide with wire clippers. At the front of the glide is a bridge that holds its top to its bottom. When you snip the bridge in two, the zipper falls apart, freeing the skin. If you try to unzip, you may pinch your skin badly.

• *Contact lenses* lost in a carpet. Place a nylon stocking over the nozzle of a vacuum cleaner and carefully vacuum the area. The lens will be pulled up onto the stocking.

• *Microwave cleaner.* Use four tablespoonfuls of baking soda to one quart of warm water. It's safer than abrasives. The same solution can clean the kitchen range, too.

• *A broken water pipe* can be patched until the plumber arrives. First shut off the water. Then cut to size a piece of thick patching rubber (or use a scrap from an inner tube, doormat or old overshoe) and wrap it around the damaged pipe. Secure the rubber with four hose clamps. You can then use the pipe temporarily with only minimal leakage.

• *Furniture scratches. For small blemishes:* Try toothpaste—its mild abrasive action is effective on minor scratches. *Deeper scratches or wide areas:* Use a blend stick, crayon, liquid shoe polish or paste boot polish. Apply toothpaste to even out the finish after coloring. Then wax with furniture polish and buff with a clean cloth.